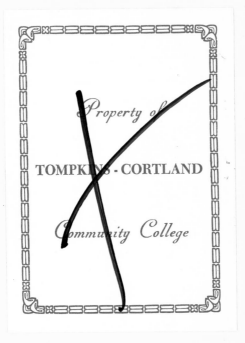

# LOGIC for Beginners
## Through Games, Jokes, and Puzzles

This is a book of games, jokes, and puzzles. But it has a serious purpose. While you play the games, laugh at the jokes, and solve the puzzles, you will be learning important things about our ways of getting knowledge.

You will find that you can learn something by seeing it yourself, by hearing about it, or by reasoning from other facts you already know. You will realize that often what you *think* you see is not what really happened, and that even more often you can't be sure of what someone else reports to you. You will see that many words have double meanings, and a badly constructed sentence can say something very different from the speaker's intention. You will learn about sets and subsets, simple and compound propositions, and relations of things. You will get some basic guidance in how to reason, how to make a valid argument, how to draw a conclusion from what you know, and how to guess at the reasons for a known conclusion.

Logic is the art of thinking clearly and straight. People learn something about logic from their daily experience. With the introduction that this book provides, you will be able to learn more and faster about how to think clearly.

# LOGIC
## For Beginners
### Through Games, Jokes, and Puzzles
Irving Adler

with
285 brain teasers
and with
205 line drawings by Ruth Adler

The John Day Company          New York

## Books by Irving Adler

COLOR IN YOUR LIFE

DUST

FIRE IN YOUR LIFE

HOT AND COLD

HOW LIFE BEGAN

INSIDE THE NUCLEUS

LOGIC FOR BEGINNERS

MAGIC HOUSE OF NUMBERS

MAN-MADE MOONS

MONKEY BUSINESS: *Hoaxes in the Name of Science*

THE NEW MATHEMATICS

PROBABILITY AND STATISTICS FOR EVERYMAN

THE SECRET OF LIGHT

SEEING THE EARTH FROM SPACE

THE STARS: *Stepping Stones into Space*

THE SUN AND ITS FAMILY

THINKING MACHINES

TIME IN YOUR LIFE

TOOLS IN YOUR LIFE

THE TOOLS OF SCIENCE

WEATHER IN YOUR LIFE

WHAT WE WANT OF OUR SCHOOLS

THE *Reason Why* BOOKS (*with Ruth Adler*)

© 1964 BY IRVING AND RUTH ADLER

The John Day Company, 257 Park Avenue South, New York, N.Y. 10010 an Intext publisher

Published on the same day in Canada by Longman Canada Limited.

*Library of Congress Catalogue Card Number:*
*64-20705*

MANUFACTURED IN THE UNITED STATES OF AMERICA

*Sixth Impression*

# Contents

# LOGIC for Beginners

# Paths to Knowledge

## Fun with a Purpose

This is a book of games, jokes, and puzzles. But it has a serious purpose. While you play the games, laugh at the jokes, and solve the puzzles, you will be learning important things about our ways of getting knowledge.

## Three Paths to Knowledge

There are three main ways of getting knowledge. These ways are illustrated in the following little story: John, Sam and Henry all say that it is raining. When they are asked how they *know* it is raining, each gives a different reply. John says, "I was just outside, and I saw that it is raining." Sam says, "John just came in from outside, and he told me that it is raining." Henry says, "I can see through the window that people are carrying open umbrellas, and I know that people carry open umbrellas only when it is raining."

Each boy got his knowledge that it is raining in a different way. John found out by direct *observation*. Sam found out by getting a *report* from somebody else who had made the direct observation. Henry found out by *reasoning* from other information that he had. The three main ways of getting knowledge are: 1) by direct observation, 2) by reports from other people, and 3) by reasoning from other knowledge. Sometimes we use one of these ways alone, but we often use all three together. We combine facts that we have observed with facts that have been reported, and then, by reasoning, we figure out new facts.

Sometimes we are free to choose any one of the three paths to knowledge, as John, Sam and Henry did in the story above. But sometimes we do not have a free choice. For example, we cannot use direct observation to learn about events that happen far away or that happened long ago. Then we must rely on reports, or on reasoning from reports.

**Booby Traps**

A man seeking knowledge is like a person trying to find his way out of a forest. There may be many paths that he can follow, but not every path will take him out of the forest. Some paths may take him around in a circle, and others may lead to a dead end. The paths that mislead him are booby traps that he should try to avoid. Similarly, there are booby traps along the paths to knowledge. There are some kinds of observation,

10

some reports, and some kinds of reasoning that cannot be trusted. In the chapters that follow we use games and puzzles to expose them, so that we may avoid the booby traps on the paths to knowledge.

### Brain Teasers

Write on a piece of paper the numbers from one to ten to represent the statements below. Next to the number for each statement write "T" if the statement is true, and "F" if the statement is false. Write "O" if your knowledge about this question is based on direct observation. Write "R" if your knowledge could be obtained only from a report. In order not to spoil the fun of anyone else who may read this book, do not write your answers in the book.

1. The sun rises in the west and sets in the east.
2. George Washington was the first President of the United States.
3. The blizzard which struck the east coast of the United States in 1888 lasted 15 days.
4. A piece of quartz can scratch the glass of a soda pop bottle.
5. All trees lose their leaves in the wintertime.
6. Milk that is kept at room temperature turns sour faster than milk that is kept cool in a refrigerator.
7. Water flows downhill.
8. At the end of 1962 the record time for a one mile run was 3 minutes 54.4 seconds.
9. The population of Vermont on April 1, 1960, was 428,213.
10. An icy pavement at freezing temperature is slippery.

# *Observation*

## Eye Witness

There are many court cases in which a jury must decide who was responsible for an accident that took place. If there are witnesses who saw the accident, they may be called to the witness stand to describe what they saw. Sometimes two witnesses, each of whom saw the accident with his own eyes, disagree in their testimony. This does not mean that one of them is lying. Each of the witnesses may be honest, and yet one or both of them may be wrong. Four games, described below, will help to show us why. To play the games, follow the directions that are given.

*The Staged Incident.* Two boys, A and B, arrange with their teacher to stage an incident in front of the class, without letting the class in on the secret. Boy A enters the class with his books held loosely under one

12

arm. Boy B is right behind A and walks close to him. Suddenly A drops his books, and, whirling around, he loudly accuses B of pushing the books out from under his arm. A fight begins that is quickly stopped by the teacher. The books are picked up, the boys take their seats, and the teacher appeals to the class to describe what happened. Very few people will know what really happened, because, although everybody saw it, *nobody was paying attention* to what he saw. However, this will not prevent the pupils in the class from thinking that they know what happened. Many different versions of the incident will probably be given. After they are all recorded, the teacher tells the class what really happened, so that they will see how unreliable eyewitness testimony can sometimes be.

*The Closed Box.* A closed box is set up in front of the classroom. The teacher has put many things into the box, and arranged them in groups. The pupils do not

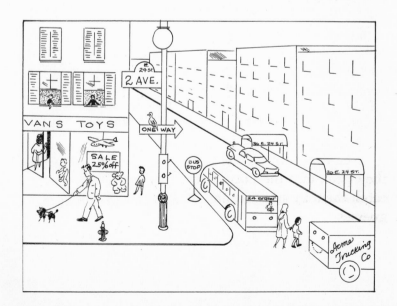

know what is in the box. The pupils are called up one at a time to raise the lid of the box and look inside for only one second. Then the teacher asks the class questions about what they saw, and each pupil writes down his answers to the questions. Suppose, for example, that these are the contents of the box: In one corner there is a piece of cloth with an unthreaded needle stuck in it. Alongside the cloth are a threaded needle, two mother-of-pearl buttons, and a cloth-covered button. In another corner there is a coiled length of clothesline rope. Behind the rope there is a drawing mounted on the wall of the box. The drawing shows a snake gliding over a rock, and a coiled snake near it. The moving snake forms a figure S. In the center of the box there are a pocket mirror, three hair pins, an open lipstick case, and a key ring with four keys on it. Questions asked about the contents might include these: How many needles are in the box? Is the needle in the cloth threaded or not threaded? How many buttons are in the box? How many buttons are cloth-covered? How many snakes are in the picture on the wall? Does the snake that is pictured as moving form a figure W, S, or C? Is the coiled thing in the corner a rope or a stuffed snake? How many hair pins are in the box? How many keys are on the key ring? Is the lipstick case closed or open? What else is in the box that has not been mentioned?

Since the pupils do not know what to look for when they peek into the box, many of these questions will catch them by surprise, and their answers will be only guesses.

*The Bus Story.* You say to a person, "This puzzle is a test of your ability in mental arithmetic. Listen carefully. A bus starts from one end of the line with 15 passengers on board. At its first stop it discharges one passenger and takes on five more. At the next stop the bus discharges five and takes on three. At the next stop it discharges two and takes on eight. When the bus stops again it discharges four and takes on none. At the next stop it discharges six and takes on four. Then 'it arrives at the end of the line, and all the passengers get off. How many stops did the bus make between the two ends of the line?" It is likely that the person listening to you will concentrate on figuring out how many passengers remain on the bus after each stop. When you finally bring the bus to the end of the line, he will be able to tell you how many people are on it, but he will not remember how many stops the bus made. With regard to this detail of the bus story, he was listening without paying attention.

*The Picture.* This is a game that you can play right now. DO NOT TURN BACK TO PAGE 13. There is a drawing on that page that was before your eyes when you read the page. Without looking at the drawing again, answer the following questions about it. Write your answers on a piece of paper.

1. What are the names of the streets that meet at the intersection shown in the picture?
2. A bus and a truck are shown in the picture. What street is each on?
3. Which vehicle, the truck or the bus, has just crossed the intersection?

4. A woman and child are crossing one of the streets. Which one are they crossing?
5. Are the woman and child holding hands?
6. How many buildings in the picture have entrance canopies?
7. On which street is the fire hydrant?
8. A man is walking a dog on one of the streets. Is the dog on a leash?
9. Are they walking toward the intersection or away from it?
10. Is someone entering the store or leaving it? Is it a man or a woman?
11. Is the child looking into the store window a boy or a girl?
12. What three toys are on display in the store window?
13. What percent off the regular price is announced for the sale in the store?
14. How many windows are visible above the store?
15. How many of these windows have their shutters open?
16. How many people are looking out of these windows?
17. What other animal besides the dog is visible in the picture?

After you have written down all your answers, turn back to page 13 to see how many of your answers are correct.

All four games show that it is not enough merely to see something to be able to report accurately what you have seen. It is also necessary to *pay attention* to what you see. Unless you purposely look for certain details

of what you see, they may escape your notice. Your recollection of these details at a later time may be accurate, or it may be mistaken. For this reason the testimony of a single witness who was a casual observer of an accident may be mistaken. However, it is usually unlikely that several witnesses, all observing the same scene independently, will make the same mistake. So, to guard against the errors that one witness may make, it is always desirable to get the testimony of several witnesses.

**Hidden Pictures**

The picture on this page shows an outdoor scene. However, there is more in the picture than you see at first glance. There are a calf, two dogs, a bear, a shoe, a cup and an electric light bulb hidden in the picture. See if you can find them.

The "hidden picture" game illustrates another important rule about observations. Sometimes you do not see something you are looking at because it is hidden by its surroundings. In order to see it, you must know what to look for, and you must actively search for it. Many of the facts about nature are like hidden pictures. The scientist who observes nature gets special training so that he will know what to look for and how to search for it.

### Seeing Is Not Always Believing

Look at the five pictures on page 19. Then answer these questions about the pictures.

Picture 1: Are the heavy black lines curved or are they straight? Are the lines on the left farther apart at the ends or in the middle? Are the lines on the right farther apart at the ends or in the middle?

Picture 2: This is a picture of a box. There are nine stripes on the top of the box. Where are the stripes farthest apart? Which line is longer, a stripe or the edge of the box marked $h$?

Picture 3: Which small square is larger, the small white square or the small black square?

Picture 4: Which line is longer, $a$ or $b$?

Picture 5: Which arrow is longer, $c$ or $d$?

Now use a ruler to check your answers. You will find that the way things *look* is not always the way they *are*. In picture 1, the heavy black lines look curved, but they are straight. The lines on the left look closer at the

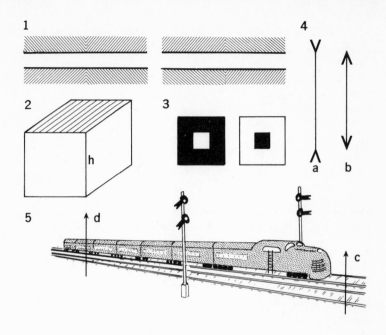

ends than at the middle, but they aren't. The lines on the right look closer in the middle than at the ends, but they aren't. In picture 2, the stripes look as if they are farther apart at the upper end than at the lower end, but they aren't. The stripes look longer than the edge *h*, but they are same length. In picture 3, the small white square looks larger than the small black square, but they are really the same size. In picture 4, line *a* looks longer than line *b*, but they are really the same length. In picture 5, arrow *d* looks longer than arrow *c*, but they are really the same length.

There is a popular saying that "Seeing is believing." These five pictures show the saying is not always true. There are times when you cannot rely on what you see with your eyes alone. To avoid being misled by your eyes, you must check what you see by using measuring instruments.

## Measuring a String

However, even observations made with measuring instruments are not foolproof. To see this fact for yourself, perform this simple experiment. Cut a piece of string long enough to reach from your shoulder to your fingertips. Then, using a foot ruler, measure the length of the string to the nearest sixteenth of an inch, and write down the measurement that you get. Measure the length of the string all over again four more separate times. Compare the five measurements that you get. Are they all the same? It is likely that they are not. In this case the measurements may be different because the string is stretchy. Scientists find that they have a similar problem with any measurement that they make. They cannot rely on a single measurement alone, because when the measurement is repeated the result may be a little different from what it was before. To get around this problem, a scientist always repeats many times any measurement that he must make. Then, to get a single reliable measure, he averages the results of his measurement.

In some occupations, such as cabinetmaking or dressmaking, the worker measures and then cuts parts that must fit together. Because a single measurement is not reliable, these workers take very seriously the old saying, "Measure ten times before you cut once."

## Cooking Carrots

A certain housewife in New York learned how to cook by trial and error. To cook carrots, she tried cooking them in boiling water in an open pot for 5 minutes, 10 minutes, 15 minutes, 20 minutes, 25 minutes, and 30 minutes. She found that carrots were underdone if they were cooked for only 5, 10, or 15 minutes, but they were tender if they were cooked for 20 minutes or more. So she wrote down in her kitchen notebook this result of her own direct observation: The cooking time for carrots is 20 minutes. Later the family moved to the country and lived on a mountain at an altitude of 10,000 feet. In their new home she began to have trouble with her cooking. Carrots cooked for 20 minutes turned out to be underdone. By trial and error she discovered that now she must cook carrots for 40 minutes instead of 20. She was puzzled by the change until her son explained it to her. The cooking time for anything depends on how hot the water is in which you cook it. The hotter the water is, the faster it cooks the things that are in it. When carrots are cooked in boiling water in an open pot, the temperature of the water is the boiling point of water. But the boiling point of water is not the same in all places. The boiling point of water depends on the atmospheric pressure, and atmospheric pressure depends on the altitude. In New York, which is at sea level, atmospheric pressure is about 15 pounds per square inch, and water boils at a temperature of 212° Fahrenheit. At an altitude of 10,000 feet, atmospheric pressure is only about 10 pounds per square inch. At this lower pressure, water boils at the lower temperature of 194°. That is why it took longer to cook the carrots. After this experience the housewife began using a cook book. In the cook book she found this rule: For cooking times at high altitudes, add 10% to the sea-level cooking time for every 1,000 feet of altitude.

This housewife's experience brings to our attention an important fact about observations. The results of an observation often depend on the conditions under which the observation is made. What may be true under one set of conditions may be false under another set of conditions. For this reason scientists perform their experiments under many different conditions, to see how a change in the conditions of an experiment affects the result.

## Summary

In this chapter we have exposed several traps that stand in the way of making reliable observations. We have also found ways of avoiding these traps:
1. Casual observation is unreliable. To get reliable information you have to pay attention to what you observe.
2. You may not see what you are looking at unless you know what you are looking for.
3. Several witnesses are better than one.
4. Our eyes and ears sometimes mislead us. To get reliable observations, we often have to use measuring instruments.
5. The results of a single measurement are not reliable. Measurements should be repeated.
6. What was observed to be true under one set of con-

ditions may be false under another set of conditions. It is important to see how the results of an observation change as conditions change.

## Brain Teasers

Write your answers to all questions on a separate sheet of paper. Do not write in the book.

1. Answer this question without looking back to check: On what page is the bus story told?
2. You looked at the table of contents when you began reading this book. Answer this question without looking at the table of contents again to check: How many chapters are there in this book?
3. John and Henry both looked for eggs of the monarch butterfly on milkweed plants. Henry is doing this for the first time. John, who raises butterflies, found many eggs on plants on which Henry didn't see any. Which rule stated on page 22 might explain why?
4. What is the cooking time for carrots at an altitude of 4,000 feet?
5. Use A, B, C, D or E to complete each sentence correctly:
   - I.   The color of an object depends on . . .
   - II.  The length of an object depends on . . .
   - III. The weight of an object depends on . . .
   - IV.  The temperature at which water boils depends on . . .
     - A. the humidity
     - B. the atmospheric pressure
     - C. the light that shines on it
     - D. the temperature
     - E. its height above sea level.

# *Reports*

## The Game of "Telephone"

In this amusing party game, the players sit in a line. The first player in the line writes a statement on a piece of paper and puts it away so that the statement cannot be seen by the other players. Then he whispers the statement into the ear of the second person in line. The second person whispers what he hears into the ear of the third person. The third person passes the message on to the fourth person, and so on, until the message reaches the end of the line. It is important to observe three rules while playing the game: 1) *Each player whispers the message softly into the ear of the next player in line, so that only the next player can hear what he says.* 2) *Each player whispers the message only once.* 3) Once the game is under way the message is usually mixed with gasps and giggles, but that does not matter. *Each player tries to hear the message as well as he can, and he tries to pass on exactly what he has heard.*

When the message reaches the end of the line, the last player writes down what he hears. Then he reads it out loud. Then the first player reads out loud the message he originally sent down the line. When you play the game you will find that the message received at the end of the line rarely resembles the original message. It gets changed in the funniest ways as it passes from mouth to mouth.

The game of telephone takes its name from a real life situation that it resembles. Mrs. A picks up some information and passes it on by telephone to Mrs. B. Mrs. B, while telephoning her friend Mrs. C, tells her what she has heard from Mrs. A. Through a chain of telephone conversations, the information is passed from mouth to mouth, and spreads through the town. Thus a *rumor* is set into motion. The outcome of the game of telephone shows you how much you can trust a rumor: Although a report may be true when it starts circulating, the version of it received by the tenth or twelfth person in the chain may be false. Whenever a statement is passed on to you with the introduction, "everybody knows that . . . ," or "they say that . . . ," or "I just heard that . . . ," be careful about accepting it as the truth. Any resemblance between the statement and the true state of affairs may be purely coincidental.

**The Missing Purse**

The picture on page 26 shows a woman shopping in

a department store. She has very unwisely put her
purse on the counter while she talks to the salesclerk.
To see why it is unwise, follow these directions: Pro-
vide yourself with a piece of white paper, a black pencil, a red pencil and a piece of red cellophane. (You
may be able to get the red cellophane from a candy
wrapper, or a milk bottle cap, etc.) Place the paper
over the picture of the department store scene. Trace
the purse with the red pencil. Trace the rest of the picture with the black pencil. When the picture is complete, look at it through the red cellophane. You will
find that the lady's purse has disappeared!

**Rose-Colored Glasses**

Suppose you were to show the two-color picture you
have drawn to two people, one of whom is wearing
ordinary eyeglasses with colorless lenses, while the
other one is wearing eyeglasses with red-tinted lenses.
The first one would report that there is a purse on the

counter. The second one would report that there is no purse there at all. The reports do not agree, even though each person reports exactly what he sees. This example shows that what you see sometimes depends on how you look at things. In this case, the red-tinted lenses used by the second person give him a bias which prevents him from seeing the purse.

If you look through red-tinted lenses, everything you see has a bright rosy hue. This is because the glasses color what you see. People's personalities have a similar effect on what they see. A person who is usually cheerful and optimistic tends to report things in a cheerful way, while a person who is usually gloomy and pessimistic tends to report things in a gloomy way. We say of the cheerful person that "he always sees the bright side of things," or that "he sees the world through rose-colored glasses." A person's personality gives him a bias that "colors" what he sees and reports. Similarly a person's reports may be colored by his opinions, his past experiences, and so on.

## Pictures in the Clouds

This is a game that you can play on a sunny day when the sky is partly cloudy. Look at the clouds as they move across the sky, and look for familiar pictures formed by the shapes and shading of the clouds. Here you may see a team of horses, there you may see an old man with a flowing white beard. If two or more people play the game together, you will find that they rarely agree on what they see in the same cloud. Where one sees a man with a beard, another may see Niagara

Falls. Where one sees a team of horses, another may see a sailboat. These disagreements give us an example of the fact that what a person sees and reports often depends on who does the seeing. Part of what a person sees and reports is contributed by the scene he looks at. But part of what he sees and reports is also contributed by his own bias.

### Ink-Blot Pictures

The drawings on page 29 were made by scattering some drops of ink on a piece of paper and then folding the paper while the ink was still wet. You can look for pictures in the ink-blot drawings in the same way that you look for pictures in the clouds. Show the drawings to your classmates or to members of your family and ask them what pictures they see in them. Write down and compare the different answers that you get.

What a person sees in an ink-blot drawing depends partly on his personality. For this reason psychologists often use ink-blot drawings as a personality test. The psychologist shows to the person being tested ten special ink-blot drawings known as Rorschach prints. What the person sees in the prints gives clues to his personality.

### The Reliability of a Report

Whenever information is passed on to us in a spoken or written report we must consider carefully whether the report is one that can be trusted. The games described in this chapter suggest some questions we

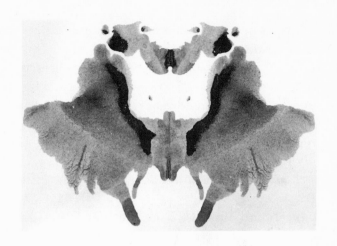

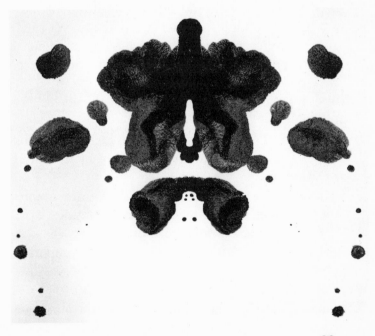

29

should keep in mind when we try to judge the reliability of a report.

1. Is the report firsthand or secondhand? A firsthand report is one that is based on what the reporter saw himself. A secondhand report is based on what the reporter heard from somebody else. A secondhand report is less reliable than a firsthand report. If the only report you can get is a secondhand report, try to check it by consulting other sources of information.

2. Is the report biased? This question is not always easy to answer. You have to know something about the reporter to know whether his bias colors his reports. Since individual reports may be biased, it is good to compare several reports by different individuals. Scientific experiments are always repeated by many different scientists in order to guard against the possibility that an unconscious bias may affect the reports of any one scientist.

Here are some other questions that should also be kept in mind:

3. Is the report up to date? For example, if population figures are quoted, do they come from the latest census report?

4. Is the person a specialist in the field he writes about? For example, an article on particle physics by a particle physicist would be more reliable than an article on particle physics by a newspaper reporter.

## Brain Teasers

1. Scientist John Doe has a favorite theory. He has just

30

reported the results of a new experiment never performed before. The results support his theory. Should you trust his report?

2. Mr. A. is writing an article about an important meeting that took place five years ago. He has read all the newspaper accounts of the meeting, and they carry conflicting reports about what happened there. What can he do to find out the truth?

3. John is preparing a report for his science class on the elementary particles of physics. He plans to base his report on an article in an encyclopedia printed fifteen years ago. Is this a good plan?

## CHAPTER IV

# Words, Statements, and Propositions

Reasoning is done through chains of statements. Each statement is a chain of words. Before you can judge whether reasoning is good or bad, you have to know what the words and statements in it mean. The games in this chapter deal with the meaning of words and statements.

## More than One Meaning

Some words have more than one meaning.

Each pair of drawings (numbered 1 to 10) pictures two different meanings of one word. What is the word? Write your answers on a separate sheet of paper. Do not write in the book.

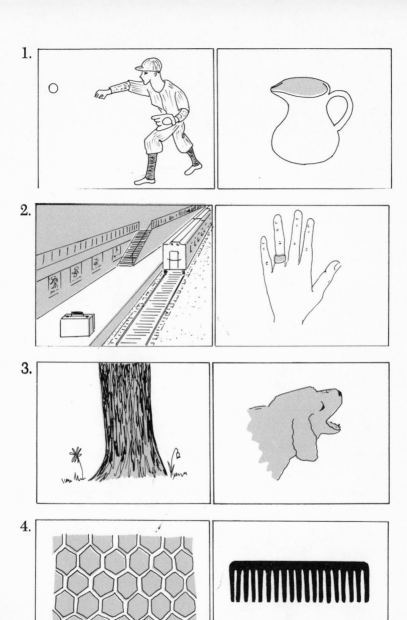

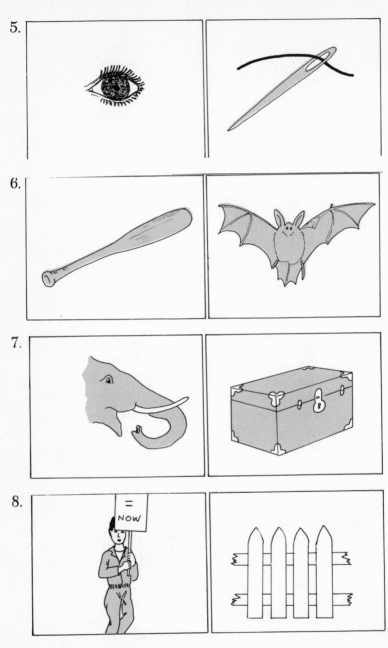

5.

6.

7.

8.

34

**9.**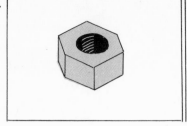

**10.**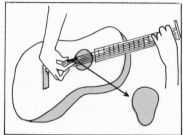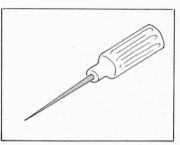

One word with two different meanings is needed to fill each pair of blank spaces. What is the word? Write your answers on a separate sheet of paper.

11. ". . .," said John, when the teacher called his name.
Each birthday . . . was wrapped in colored paper and tied with a ribbon.

12. The rabbit plunged into the . . . .
The . . . had stiff nylon bristles.

13. The knight wore a glittering coat of . . . .
The . . . is delivered once a day on the rural route.

14. To save gas, they organized a car . . . .
He dove into the . . . with a splash.

15. It is rude to . . . .
The tack had a sharp . . . .

16. (With apologies to Omar Khayyam)
What fun it would be

To . . . under a tree
With a jug of wine, a . . . of bread
And thee.

17. The . . . lifted the queen's train from the ground.
There were about 300 words on each . . . .

18. Both children screamed, "It's . . . !" as each
tugged at an arm of the doll.
Their faces covered with coal dust,
the men trudged home from the . . . .

19. The jury delivered its verdict in the . . . .
A . . . of soda pop was ordered for the party.

20. Don't . . . the boat.
Every . . . , no matter how hard, can be worn down
by wind and water.

## Meaning in a Context

When a word is used in a sentence or paragraph, the rest of the sentence or paragraph is called its *context*. Although the word by itself may have many different meanings, we can often tell from the context which meaning it is intended to have in the sentence or paragraph. For example, the word *rock* may mean *to move back and forth,* but it may also mean a *mass of stone.* In the sentence, *Don't rock the boat,* we can see from the context that *rock* has the first of these two meanings.

For each sentence below, two possible meanings, labeled *a* and *b*, are listed for the missing word. What is the word, and which meaning does it have in that sentence? Write your answers on a separate sheet of paper. Do not write in the book.

21. He had a spare . . . in the trunk of the car.
    a. To become weary.
    b. A rubber cushion fitted around the rim of a wheel.
22. The . . . landed on his jaw.
    a. A forcible stroke delivered with a part of the body or with an instrument.
    b. To produce a current of air.
23. He pitched two strikes and a . . . in succession.
    a. A spherical body.
    b. A pitched ball in baseball that is not struck at by the batter and that fails to pass over some portion of the home plate not higher than the batter's armpit or lower than his knees or that touches the ground before passing over home plate.
24. He spread raspberry . . . on his bread.
    a. A crowded mass of people or things causing impedance or blockage.
    b. A product made by boiling fruit and sugar to a thick consistency without preserving the shape of the fruit.
25. The child sat on his mother's . . . .
    a. The front part of the lower trunk and thighs of a seated person.
    b. To scoop up food and drink with the tip of the tongue.
26. The baby takes a . . . every afternoon.
    a. A soft, fuzzy, fibrous surface.
    b. A short sleep.
27. He turned the key in the . . . .

a. A tuft, tress, or ringlet of hair as it grows.

b. A fastening.

28. The . . . was ground into flour at the mill.

   a. The unhusked or the threshed seeds or fruits of various food plants.

   b. The appearance and texture of wood.

29. If you don't come soon, I'll tan your . . . .

   a. To conceal.

   b. The skin of a human being.

30. The sauce is a . . . too sweet.

   a. The smallest or an insignificant amount or degree.

   b. The biting or cutting edge or part of a tool.

## Double Meanings

Sometimes the context of a word allows it to have two different meanings. A sentence in which a word has a double meaning is a common type of joke. Some advertising slogans use a double meaning to attract attention and make a lasting impression. For example, one salt company uses the slogan, "When it rains, it pours." The state police (troopers) of Connecticut, in their campaign against drunken driving, have posted signs along the roads saying, "He who takes one for the road gets trooper for chaser." Here are some other funny statements in which a word or phrase has a double meaning. Which word or phrase in each statement has the double meaning?

31. He liked his job very much. He was fired with enthusiasm.

32. There were many vegetables in the stew, but the meat was rare.

38

33. The surgeon opened his chest and put the tools in one by one.
34. Instead of rotating their crops, the peasants kept raising cane.
35. Every morning the boxer was taken for a walk.
36. He spotted a leopard in the forest.
37. The clock struck one.
38. He did his homework with great pains.

(See the drawings on page 40.)

## The Little Moron

The popular "little moron" jokes have a special twist. Each joke consists of a question and an answer. The answer by itself has *one* clear meaning. But, when it is put alongside the question, it acquires *another* meaning that makes it sound funny. Here are some examples:

Why did the little moron start a fire in the forest?
Because he wanted to blaze a trail.

Why did the little moron soak his kite in whiskey?
Because he wanted it to fly high.

Why did the little moron actor play pool backstage?
So he wouldn't miss his cue.

Why did the little moron blow on his baseball?
Because he was a baseball fan.

Why did the little moron lock his father in the refrigerator?
Because he wanted cold pop.

35

36

37

38

40

Why did the little moron smash his piano?
So he could get a key for his door.

Why did the little moron sit on his watch as he drove to
work?
So he would be on time.

Try to make up some little moron jokes of your own.

**Did You Ever See . . . ?**

Another type of joke, beginning with the words "did
you ever see . . . ," gets its double meaning from the
fact that the last word in the question may be understood as either a noun or a verb. Here are some examples:
Did you ever see a jelly roll?
Did you ever see a diamond ring?
Did you ever see a cow hide?
Did you ever see a house fly?

Did you ever see a paper box?
Did you ever see a lamb chop?
Did you ever see a foot rule?
Did you ever see a home run?
Did you ever see a sea coast?
Try to make up your own "Did you ever see" jokes.

## Poorly Constructed Sentences

The meaning of a sentence does not depend only on the meanings of the words in the sentence. It depends also on how the words are combined in the sentence. For example, these two sentences which use the same words have totally different meanings: 1) The man wore a dark hat. 2) The dark man wore a hat. In one case the word *dark* is combined with the word *hat* to describe a quality of the hat. In the other case it is combined with the word *man* to describe a quality of the man.

A well-constructed sentence shows clearly how the words in it are supposed to be combined. A poorly constructed sentence sometimes allows the words to be combined in two different ways. Then the sentence may have a funny double meaning. For example, consider the sentence, "One minute after Mrs. Green christened the ship, she was afloat on the river." Because of the way the words are arranged in the sentence, the word *she* may refer to the ship or to Mrs. Green. The double meaning can be eliminated by rewriting the sentence as follows: One minute after Mrs. Green christened it, the ship was afloat on the river.

A sentence that has a double meaning is said to be *ambiguous*. Each of the following sentences is ambiguous because the sentence is poorly constructed. Rewrite the sentence in two ways to show clearly, one at a time, each of the two meanings it may have.

39. A boy who comes late often is required to bring a parent to school.
40. The skies are not cloudy all day.
41. She removed the rug from the room and swept it.

In the following ambiguous sentences, only one of the two possible meanings is obviously intended. Rewrite each sentence so that it expresses clearly only the intended meaning.

42. He called the dog, put the newspaper in his mouth, and started back home.
43. Every morning he takes a run followed by a shower bath.
44. The police department closed its books today in the case of Jane Grant, daughter of Dr. Samuel Grant, who disappeared seven years ago.
45. When six years old, my grandfather died.

**Universe of Discourse**

Mary came home from school and said to her mother, "Jane had her hair cut yesterday." Her mother asked, "Which Jane do you mean, the one in your class, or the one who lives on this block?" In order to make her meaning clear, Mary had to say whether the Jane she was talking about belonged to the group of children in her class or to the group of children who live on her block. This example illustrates an important rule. Whenever you talk about persons or things, it helps to make your meaning clear if you specify some set or group to which the persons or things belong. The set to which the persons or things you talk about belong is called a *universe of discourse* for your statement. For example, if you use the word *vowels* we know that you are referring to certain letters of an alphabet. But it is not clear which letters are referred to unless you specify which alphabet you are talking about. If the universe of discourse is the English alphabet, then the vowels are the letters *a*, *e*, *i*, *o*, and *u*.

Any set of things which includes the things you are talking about may be chosen as a universe of discourse for your statements. Choose a possible universe of discourse for the things or people referred to by each of these terms:

46. Vermonters      47. green      48. table
49. pencil      50. boy

## Sets and Subsets

Any group of things in a universe of discourse is called a *set* in that universe of discourse. Sometimes a set may be specified by a descriptive phrase. For example, in the universe of discourse that consists of all children, the descriptive phrase "blonde-haired and blue-eyed" specifies a particular set of children. A set may sometimes be specified by using a single word. For example, in the universe of discourse that consists of all children the word *boys* refers to the set of all male children. The word *girls* refers to the set of all female children.

If all the members of a set are included among the members of a second set, we say that the first set is a *subset* of the second set. For example, the set of all blonde boys is a subset of the set of all boys. The set of all blue-eyed children is not a subset of the set of all boys, because not all blue-eyed children are boys.

The universe of discourse for exercises 51 to 57 consists of the following printed capital letters of the English alphabet: A, B, C, D, E, F, G, H, I, J, K, L, M, N, O, P, Q, R, S, T, U, V, W, X, Y, Z.

51. List the members of the set each of which has at least one closed loop. (Closed loop set)
52. List the members of the set each of which has exactly one closed loop. (One closed loop set)
53. List the members of the set each of which is made

with straight lines only. (Straight line set)

54. List the members of the set each of which is made with exactly two straight lines. (Two straight lines set)

55. List the members of the set each of which is made with exactly three straight lines. (Three straight lines set)

56. Is the "one closed loop set" a subset of the "closed loop set?"

57. Is the "two straight lines set" a subset of the "three straight lines set?"

## Asserting a Property of a Set

We often make statements in which we assert that certain things have a particular property. For example, in the statement "all dogs have four legs," we assert that the animals called *dogs* have the property that *each has four legs*. A statement like this can always be understood as an assertion about sets in a universe of discourse. In this case, for example, let the universe of discourse consist of *all animals*. There is a set in this universe of discourse that consists of all animals that are dogs. Let us call this set the set A. Another set in this same universe of discourse consists of all animals that have four legs. Let us call this set the set B. The statement that "all dogs have four legs" asserts that the members of set A are included among the members of set B. That is, set A is a subset of set B. In the same way, any statement that certain things have a particular property can be understood to assert that in an appropriate universe of discourse one set (the set of

46

given things) is a subset of another set (the set of things that have that particular property).

Each of the following statements can be understood to assert that in a certain universe of discourse a set A is a subset of a set B. In each case identify the universe of discourse, the set A, and the set B.

58. All birds have wings.
59. All insects have six legs.
60. All frogs can swim.

## Definitions

Two boys were playing boxball, a game in which a rubber ball is hit back and forth between two adjacent squares. When the ball landed on the line at the outer edge of a square, there was a big argument about whether or not the ball was *out*. The boy who had last hit the ball said a line ball is "good." The other boy insisted that a line ball is "out." There is a simple way of avoiding arguments like this: Agree on the rules of the game before you begin to play. The rules should include a clear definition of the word *out* as used in the game, so that you can tell without any doubt which balls are out and which balls are not out.

A similar procedure is followed in many areas of practical life, such as law and science. To avoid confusion about what a word is intended to mean we give a *definition* of the word. For example, in geometry, to explain what is meant by a triangle, we give the definition, "A triangle is a polygon with three sides." We can learn the characteristics of a good definition by observing this one. First, the definition concerns things in a particular universe of discourse. In this case the universe of discourse may be taken to be the set of all geometric figures. The word *triangle* that is being defined refers to a particular set of figures in this universe of discourse, the set of all triangles. The definition tells us first that the set of triangles is a subset of a larger set, the set of polygons. But, since not all polygons are triangles, the definition goes on to specify a property by which triangles can be distinguished from all other polygons. The distinguishing property is that of having three sides. In general, to define a term that denotes a particular set in a universe of discourse, we do two things: 1) specify in the universe of discourse a larger set of which the given set is a subset; 2) specify a property that distinguishes members of the given set from all other members of the larger set. For example, the set of Hoosiers is a subset of the set of Americans. What distinguishes Hoosiers from other Americans is that they live in Indiana. So we can define Hoosier by saying, "A Hoosier is an American who lives in Indiana."

In each of the following definitions, a) what set is denoted by the word being defined; b) what larger set is it a subset of; c) what property distinguishes members of the given set from all other members of the larger set?

61. A quadrilateral is a polygon with four sides.
62. A chair is a seat with a back and four legs.
63. Ultraviolet rays are electromagnetic rays whose wavelength is shorter than that of visible light and longer than that of x-rays.

A student who was asked, "What is a square?", replied, "A square is a quadrilateral whose sides are equal." This definition is not good, because, while it correctly states that a square is a quadrilateral, it doesn't list enough properties of a square to distinguish those quadrilaterals that are squares from those that are not squares. The figure below, for example, is a quadrilateral whose sides are equal, but it is not a square. The definition can be corrected by saying, "A

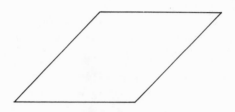

square is a quadrilateral whose sides are equal and whose angles are right angles."

Each of the definitions below is not good, because it gives too little information about the term being defined. Write a corrected definition to take its place.

64. A rectangle is a quadrilateral.
65. The number 3 is more than 2.

## Asserting a Property of an Individual

In some statements we assert that an *individual person or thing* has a particular property. In such statements we are really making two assertions at the same time: We are asserting that: 1) there is such a person or thing in the universe of discourse, and that 2) this person or thing is a member of a certain set in that universe of discourse. Consider, for example, the statement, "John has blue eyes." Let the universe of discourse be the set of people I know. The statement "John has blue eyes" asserts:

1) Among the people I know there is a person called John;
2) This person belongs to the set of people I know who have blue eyes.

Each of the following statements can be understood to make two assertions: 1) that there is a certain individual in the universe of discourse; 2) that this individual is a member of a certain set. For each statement, describe an appropriate universe of discourse, and write out the two assertions.

66. Fred sits next to me in class.
67. John plays first base.

## Asserting a Relation

In the preceding paragraphs we examined two types of common statements. One type concerns two sets in a universe of discourse, and asserts that one set is a subset of the other. The second type concerns an individual and a set in a universe of discourse, and asserts that the individual exists and is a member of the set. There is a third type of statement that concerns two or more individuals in a universe of discourse, and asserts that these individuals exist and that there is a certain relation that exists among them. As examples we examine some statements about just two individuals. Consider, for instance, the statement "John is Fred's brother." The universe of discourse might be the set of boys who live on this block. The statement asserts: 1) There are two boys on this block named John and Fred; and 2) John has the relation "is the brother of" to Fred. Consider next the statement "Sam is older than Tom." The universe of discourse might be the set of children in a certain family. The statement asserts: 1) There are two children in the family named Sam and Tom; and 2) Sam has the relation "is older than" to Tom. Finally, consider the statement "John loves Mary." The universe of discourse might be the set of children in the fifth-grade class. The statement asserts: 1) There are two children in the class named John and Mary; and 2) John has the relation "loves" to Mary.

Each statement below asserts that two individuals exist in a universe of discourse and that there is a particular relation between them. What is the relation that connects the first individual to the second one?

68. Mary runs faster than Jane.
69. Mrs. Green is Edward's mother.
70. Two is less than three.

## What's Wrong with the Picture?

When you gather information by observation, it is not enough merely to look at *things*. It is necessary to look for the relations between the things. To test how well you observe the relations among ordinary things, look at the pictures on pages 52 to 54. In each case, see if you can tell what is wrong with the picture.

51

71.

72.

73.

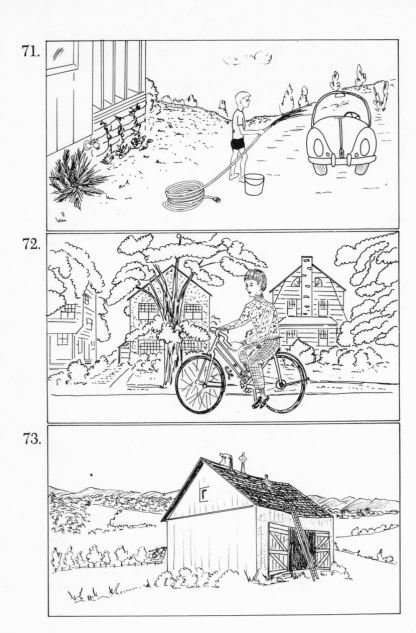

**74.**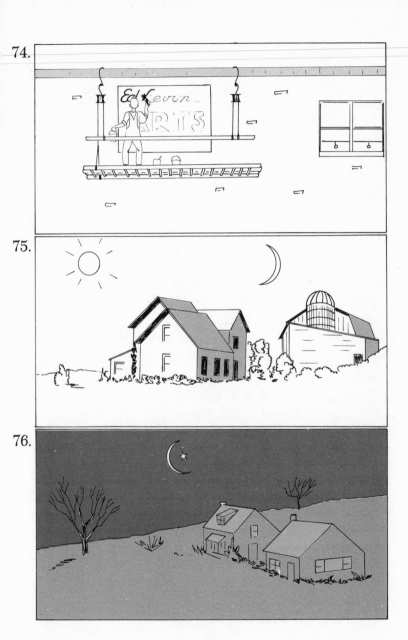

**75.**

**76.**

53

**77.**

### Find the Pattern

Here is another test of your ability to see relationships. In each of these series of numbers below, the relations of each term of the series to the terms that follow it form a pattern. Find the pattern, and then write the next four terms of the series. Write your answers on a separate sheet of paper. Do not write in the book.

78. 0, 1, 2, 3, 0, 1, 2, 3, 0, 1, 2, 3, . . . .
79. 0, 3, 6, 9, 0, 3, 6, 9, 0, 3, 6, 9, . . . .
80. 5, 4, 10, 9, 15, 14, 20, 19, . . . .
81. 1, 2, 3, 4, 5, 6, 7, . . . .
82. 1, 3, 5, 7, 9, 11, . . . .
83. 1, 4, 9, 16, 25, . . . .
84. 1, 3, 2, 4, 3, 5, 4, 6, 5, . . . .
85. 2, 6, 12, 20, 30, 42, 56, . . . .
86. 1, 3, 6, 10, 15, 21, 28, . . . .
87. 1, 1, 2, 4, 3, 9, 4, 16, 5, 25, . . . .
88. 1, 1, 2, 3, 5, 8, 13, 21, . . . .
89. 2, 4, 8, 16, 32, . . . .
90. 1, 4, 6, 7, 10, 12, 13, 16, 18, 19, . . . .

91. 1, 3, 2, 5, 7, 4, 9, 11, 6, . . . .
92. 1, 1, 2, 4, 3, 27, 4, 256, . . . .

Find the pattern in each series of pictures, and draw on a separate sheet of paper the next two pictures in the series.

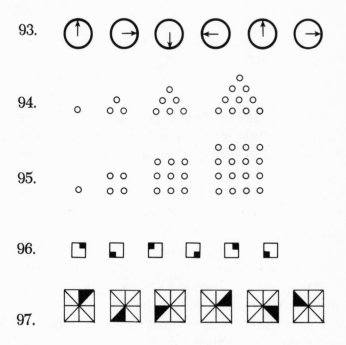

93.

94.

95.

96.

97.

Find the pattern in each series of words, and write on a separate sheet of paper the next word in the series.
98. good, bad, smooth, rough, strong, weak, tall, . . . .

99. for, four, grate, great, mien, mean, two, too, weigh, . . . .
100. bear, cub, dog, puppy, cat, kitten, cow, . . . .
101. cow, milk, sheep, wool, hog, bristles, moth, silk, bee, . . . .
102. horse, trot, cow, walk, bird, fly, snake, crawl, fish, . . . .

## Sense and Nonsense

Some statements make sense, and some are nonsense. For example, the statement "3 is greater than 2" has a meaning, and it is a true statement. The statement "2 is greater than 3" has a meaning, and it is a false statement. But the statement "red is greater than blue" has no meaning, because the relation "is greater than" does not apply to colors. The statement "red has a longer wavelength than blue" has a meaning, and it is a true statement. The statement "blue has a longer wavelength than red" has a meaning, and it is a false statement. But the statement "5 has a longer wavelength than 3" has no meaning, because the relation "has a longer wavelength than" does not apply to numbers. When the universe of discourse (or what you are talking about) is a set of numbers, a statement has meaning if it asserts a relation that can apply to numbers. The statement has no meaning if it asserts a relation that does not apply to numbers. If the universe of discourse (or what you are talking about) is a set of colors, a statement has meaning if it asserts a relation that can apply to colors. The statement has no meaning if it asserts a relation that does not apply to colors. In general, if a statement asserts a relation that can apply to members of the universe of discourse, the statement has meaning. If it asserts a relation that cannot apply to members of the universe of discourse, the statement has no meaning. Statements that have no meaning are called *nonsense*. Statements that have meaning are called *propositions*. A proposition may be either *true* or *false*. Say whether each of these statements is nonsense or a proposition. Where you have enough information about a proposition to decide, say whether the proposition is true or false. In order to give other readers a chance to answer, too, do not write your answers in the book.

103. John is older than his brother.
104. The number 2 is double 5.
105. Of all the counting numbers, 7 has the sweetest smell.
106. Di Maggio hit a hole-in-one in the fifth inning.
107. A uranium atom is heavier than a hydrogen atom.
108. Dogs are more ethical than cats.
109. Chimpanzees are more intelligent than dogs.
110. A whale is a fish.
111. The number 7 is more than the number 6.
112. When you divide a cat by a rat, the remainder is a mouse.
113. Pine wood is soft, but cherry wood is hard.
114. When two bodies fall to the ground, their paths must be parallel.
115. Red is east of blue.

## CHAPTER V

# *Sets*

We shall find it convenient to use both symbols and diagrams to represent sets. For example, suppose we are talking about the set of horses in the universe of discourse that consists of all animals. We may use the capital letter "U" to represent the universe of discourse, and the capital letter "H" to represent the set of all horses. We draw a rectangle to represent the universe of discourse. Inside the rectangle we draw a circle to represent the set of horses. Each point inside the circle represents a member of the set. The diagram is shown below.

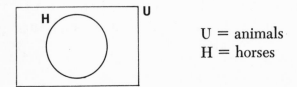

U = animals
H = horses

Use symbols and a diagram to represent each of the following sets:

1. The set of all American citizens in the universe of discourse that consists of all residents of the United States;
2. The set of all males in the universe of discourse that consists of all residents of Chicago;
3. The set of all animals in the universe of discourse that consists of all living things.

**The Empty Set**

We may draw a diagram to represent the set of all horses, and a similar diagram to represent the set of all unicorns, as follows:

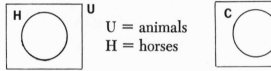
U = animals
H = horses

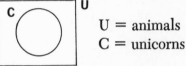
U = animals
C = unicorns

Except for the labels "H" and "C," the diagrams look alike. However, there is an important distinction between the set of horses and the set of unicorns. There actually are such things as horses, and there are no such things as unicorns. That is, the set of horses actually contains some members, but the set of unicorns does not contain any members at all. The set of unicorns is empty. There is a way of showing this distinction in a diagram. To express the proposition "there are some horses," we put an asterisk ( * ) in the circle that represents the set of horses. The asterisk in

59

the circle shows that the set is not empty. To express the proposition "there are no unicorns," we shade the circle that represents the set of unicorns. The shading in the circle shows that the set is empty. The diagram for each proposition is shown below:

There are some horses.　　　There are no unicorns.

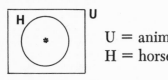 U = animals
H = horses

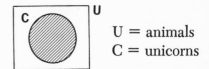 U = animals
C = unicorns

Use symbols and a diagram to represent each of the following propositions. The universe of discourse in each case is the set of all animals.

4. There are no three-legged robins.
5. There are some monkeys.
6. There are no phoenixes.

**The Complement of a Set**

Whenever a set S is defined in a universe of discourse the definition divides the universe into two parts. One part consists of the members of the set S. The other part consists of the members of the universe that are not in the set S. They make up the membership of a second set. This second set is called the complement of S, abbreviated as Comp S. For example, let the universe of discourse U = animals. Let the set H = horses.

Then Comp H is the set of all animals that are not horses. These animals may be referred to briefly as non-horses. In the diagram, where a rectangle represents U, and a circle inside the rectangle represents H, the part of the rectangle that is outside the circle represents Comp H.

Supply the missing information in each line below. In each case U stands for the universe of discourse.

7. U = living things      A = animals   Comp A = ?
8. U = residents of U.S.    C = citizens   Comp C = ?
9. U = population of U.S.   A = adults     Comp A = ?

To represent by a diagram the proposition "there are some nonhorses," let H = horses, draw the diagram for H, and put an asterisk in the space that represents Comp H.

There are some nonhorses.

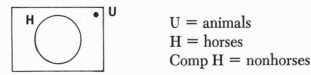

U = animals
H = horses
Comp H = nonhorses

To represent by a diagram the proposition "there are no nonhorses," let H = horses, draw the diagram for H, and shade the space that represents Comp H.

There are no nonhorses.

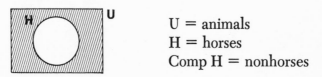

U = animals
H = horses
Comp H = nonhorses

61

Notice that a proposition does not have to be true in order to have a diagram. The diagram is merely a pictorial way of saying the proposition, and the proposition itself may be either true or false.

Copy each of the following diagrams and complete it so that it will represent the given proposition.

10. There are some living things that are not animals.

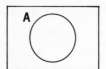

U = living things
A = animals
Comp A = nonanimals

11. There are no noncitizens living in the United States.

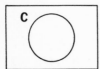

U = residents of the U.S.
C = citizens
Comp C = noncitizens

12. There are no children in the United States.

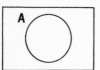

U = population of the U.S.
A = adults
Comp A = nonadults (children)

62

Each of the diagrams below represents a proposition. What is the proposition? (The proposition need not be true.)

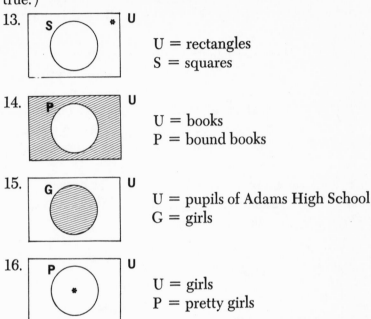

13.

U = rectangles
S = squares

14.

U = books
P = bound books

15.

U = pupils of Adams High School
G = girls

16.

U = girls
P = pretty girls

## Two Sets

Sometimes we deal with two different sets that are in the same universe of discourse. The possible relations between the sets can be shown by means of a diagram. In the diagram below, one circle represents the set S, and the other circle represents the set T, both of

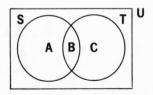

which are in the universe of discourse U. Notice that the set T divides the set S into two parts, labeled A and B; also, the set S divides the set T into two parts, labeled B and C. The three parts, A, B, and C may be described as follows:

A consists of those members of S that are not in T.

B consists of those members of the universe that are in both S and T.

C consists of those members of T that are not in S.

Part B, which consists of the members of the universe that are in both S and T, is called the *intersection* of S and T.

Each of the parts A, B, or C may be either empty or not empty. Examples of typical possibilities are given below, with a diagram for each.

Example I:

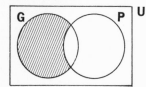

U = animals
P = people
G = girls

*All girls are people.* That is, the set of girls is a subset of the set of people. So, in this case, part A is empty. This statement is shown in the diagram by the shading in part A.

Example II:

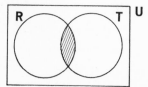

U = animals
R = robins
T = three-legged animals

*There are no robins that have three legs.* So in this case part B is empty. This statement is shown in the diagram by the shading in part B.

Example III:

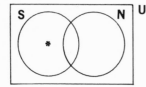

U = political units
S = states of the United States
N = states in North America

*There is at least one state of the United States that is not in North America, namely Hawaii.* So, in this case, part A is not empty. This statement is shown in the diagram by the asterisk in part A.

Example IV:

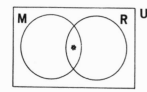

U = people
M = movie actors
R = rich people

*Some movie actors are rich.* So, in this case, part B is not empty. This statement is shown in the diagram by an asterisk in part B.

Let S and T be two different sets in a universe of discourse U. Draw a diagram to represent each of the following statements:

17. There are no members of S in T.
18. All members of S are members of T. (S is a subset of T.)
19. Some members of S are not in T.
20. Some members of S are in T.

## CHAPTER VI

# Simple Propositions

## Compound and Simple Propositions

Some propositions consist of two or more propositions joined by the connecting words *and, or,* or *if.* Because they are made by joining other propositions they are called *compound* propositions. Here are some examples.

*John is tall, and his sister is short.* In this proposition, the two propositions, "John is tall" and "his sister is short," are joined by the word *and.*

*Either he is not coming, or he will be late.* In this proposition, the two propositions, "he is not coming" and "he will be late," are joined by the word *or.*

*I shall come to your party if you invite me.* In this proposition, the two propositions, "I shall come to your party" and "you invite me," are joined by the word *if.*

A proposition that is not compound is called *simple*. For example, the proposition *"John is tall"* is simple.

State whether each of these propositions is simple or compound. Do not write your answer in the book.

1. The sun rises in the east and it sets in the west.
2. I think I passed my examination.
3. Ice is frozen water.
4. If the pressure in the boiler is above 30 pounds, it may explode.
5. Either it actually happened, or I saw it in a dream.

In this chapter we shall get acquainted with the main kinds of simple propositions. In Chapter VIII we deal with ways of reasoning with simple propositions. We shall not take up reasoning with compound propositions in this book at all.

### All A Are B

The proposition "all dogs are animals" is a statement about two sets, the set of things called *dogs* and the set of things called *animals*. The proposition says that all members of the first set are members of the second set. Using the scheme described in Chapter V, we can draw a diagram as follows to represent the proposition:

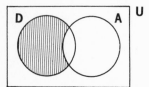

U = living things
D = dogs
A = animals

The proposition "all dogs are animals" has the form "all A are B," where A and B are sets. A similar diagram can be used to represent any proposition that has this form.

Draw a diagram for each of these propositions:

6. All grasses are plants. (Let U = living things.)
7. All cats are mammals. (Let U = animals.)
8. All mice are rodents. (Let U = animals.)

Write in the form "All A are B" the proposition represented by each of these diagrams:

9.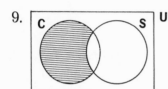

U = furniture
C = chairs
S = seats

10.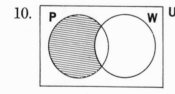

U = office supplies
P = pencils
W = writing implements

11.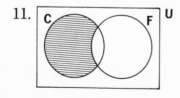

U = animals
C = cows
F = four-legged animals

## No A Are B

The proposition "no dogs are cats" is a statement about two sets, the set of things called *dogs* and the set of things called *cats*. The proposition says that the intersection of the two sets is empty. The proposition can be represented by the following diagram:

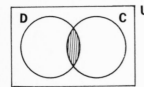

U = animals
D = dogs
C = cats

The proposition "no dogs are cats" has the form "no A are B," where A and B are sets. A similar diagram can be used to represent any proposition that has this form.

Draw a diagram for each of these propositions:

12. No boys are girls. ( U = people )
13. No circles are triangles. ( U = plane figures )
14. No pillows are hard (things). ( U = home furnishings )

Write in the form "no A are B" the proposition represented by each of these diagrams:

15.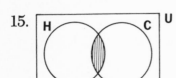

U = animals
H = horses
C = horned animals

70

**16.**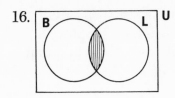

U = people
B = boys
L = liars

**17.**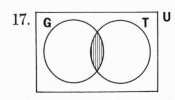

U = pupils
G = girls
T = truants

## Some A Are B

The proposition "some men are baseball players" is a statement about two sets, the set of *men* and the set of *baseball players*. The proposition says that the intersection of the two sets is not empty. The proposition can be represented by the following diagram:

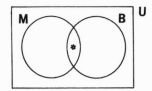

U = people
M = men
B = baseball players

The proposition "some men are baseball players" has the form "some A are B," where A and B are sets. A similar diagram can be used to represent any proposition that has this form.

Draw a diagram for each of these propositions:

18. Some boys are liars. ( U = people)

19. Some businessmen are thieves. (U = people)
20. Some thieves are murderers. (U = people)

Write in the form "some A are B" the proposition represented by each of these diagrams:

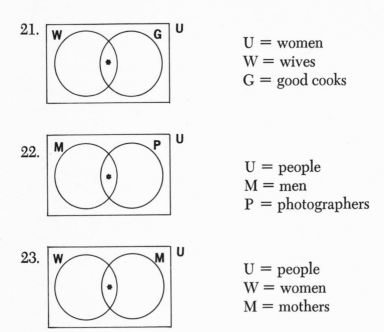

21.

U = women
W = wives
G = good cooks

22.

U = people
M = men
P = photographers

23.

U = people
W = women
M = mothers

**Some A Are Not B**

The proposition "some girls are not good company" is a statement about two sets, the set of *girls* and the set of people who are *good company*. The proposition says that the intersection of the set of girls and the complement of the set of people who are good company is not empty. The proposition can be represented by the following diagram:

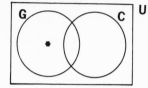

U = people
G = girls
C = good company

The proposition "some girls are not good company" has the form "some A are not B," where A and B are sets. A similar diagram can be used to represent any proposition that has this form.

Draw a diagram for each of these propositions:

24. Some men are not thieves. ( U = people )
25. Some flying animals are not birds. ( U = animals )
26. Some cats are not dogs. ( U = animals )

Write in the form "some A are not B" the proposition represented by each of these diagrams:

27.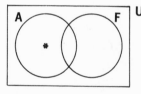

U = people
A = acquaintances
F = friends

28.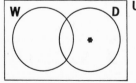

U = animals
D = ducks
W = wild animals

73

29.

U = people
A = Americans
F = farmers

## X Is a B

The proposition "Shakespeare is an Englishman" is a statement about an individual, *Shakespeare,* and the set of people called *Englishmen.* We saw on page 49 that this kind of proposition makes two assertions at the same time: 1) the individual exists in the universe of discourse; 2) the individual is a member of the set.

We can also interpret the proposition as a statement about *two sets* in this way: one set is the set of people whose only member is Shakespeare; the other set is the set of Englishmen. This interpretation gives a new meaning to each of the assertions 1) and 2): 1) the first set is not empty; 2) all members of the first set are members of the second set.

These new versions of assertions 1) and 2) tell us how to draw a diagram for the proposition. Since assertion 2) has the form "all A are B," we first draw the diagram for that type of proposition. Since assertion 1) says the set whose only member is Shakespeare is not empty, we put an asterisk into the unshaded part of the circle that represents this set.

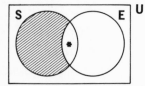

U = people
S = Shakespeare
E = Englishmen

74

The proposition "Shakespeare is an Englishman" has the form "X is a B," where X is an individual person or thing and B is a set. A similar diagram can be used to represent any proposition that has this form. In the diagram, the individual person or thing is represented as a set that has that person or thing as its only member. An asterisk is used to show that the set is not empty.

Draw a diagram for each of these propositions:

30. The baby is a boy. ( U = children )

31. New York is a city. ( U = political units )

32. The tree at the corner is an elm tree. ( U = trees )

Write in the form "X is a B" the proposition represented by each of these diagrams:

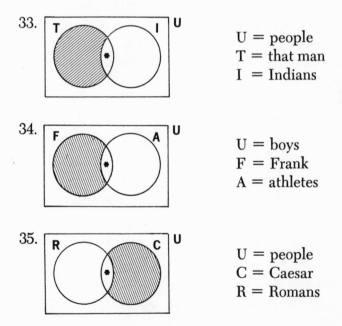

33.

U = people
T = that man
I = Indians

34.

U = boys
F = Frank
A = athletes

35.

U = people
C = Caesar
R = Romans

## X Is Not a B

The proposition "John is not a thief" is a statement about an individual, *John,* and about the set of *thieves.* This kind of proposition makes two assertions at the same time: 1) the individual exists in the universe of discourse; 2) the individual is not a member of the set.

We can also interpret the proposition as a statement about two sets in this way: one set is the set of people whose only member is John; the other set is the set of thieves. This interpretation gives a new meaning to each of the assertions 1) and 2): 1) the first set is not empty; 2) no members of the first set are members of the second set.

These new versions of assertions 1) and 2) tell us how to draw a diagram for the proposition. Since assertion 2) has the form "no A are B," we first draw the diagram for that type of proposition. Since assertion 1) says the set whose only member is John is not empty, we put an asterisk into the unshaded part of the circle that represents this set.

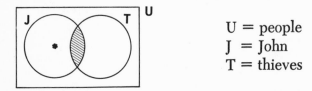

U = people
J = John
T = thieves

The proposition "John is not a thief" has the form "X is not a B," where X is an individual person or thing and B is a set. A similar diagram can be used to represent any proposition that has this form. In the diagram, the individual person or thing is represented as a set that has that person or thing as its only member. An asterisk is used to show that the set is not empty.

Draw a diagram for each of these propositions:

36. Mr. Jones is not a salesman. ( U = people )
37. This tree is not a pine tree. ( U = trees )
38. Bob is not an athlete. ( U = boys )

Write in the form "X is not a B" the proposition represented by each of these diagrams:

39.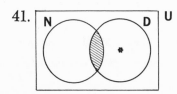

U = school subjects
T = typing
R = required subjects

40.

U = boys
P = Peter
D = good dancers

41.

U = fibers
D = dacron
N = natural fibers

**Standard Form**

We have listed six different kinds of simple propositions, having these forms:

> All A are B.
> No A are B.
> Some A are B.
> Some A are not B.
> X is a B.
> X is not a B.

These six forms are called the *standard forms* of simple propositions. If a simple proposition doesn't have one of these forms, we can in many cases rewrite it in different words so that it does, and still has the same meaning as the original proposition. Here are some examples:

1) Boys like to play baseball. *In standard form:* All boys are people who like to play baseball. (*All A are B.*)

2) Anyone who takes a dare is foolish. *In standard form:* All people who take a dare are foolish people. (*All A are B.*)

3) If he has a ticket, he is admitted. *In standard form:* All people with tickets are people who are admitted. (*All A are B.*)

4) Only boys who have passed every subject may play on a team. *In standard form:* All boys who may play on a team are boys who have passed every subject. (*All A are B.*)

5) Well-trained dogs are never disobedient. *In standard form:* No well-trained dogs are disobedient dogs. (*No A are B.*)

78

6) No person is both a good student and a social butterfly. *In standard form:* No good students are social butterflies. (*No A are B.*)

7) There is nothing in the box except potatoes. *In standard form:* No nonpotatoes are things in the box. (*No A are B.*)

Here are seven statements that have different meanings:

> One boy is on the honor roll.
> Two boys are on the honor roll.
> A few boys are on the honor roll.
> Many boys are on the honor roll.
> Most boys are on the honor roll.
> Almost all boys are on the honor roll.
> All boys but one are on the honor roll.

Part of the meaning of each of these seven statements is that "some boys are on the honor roll." In some kinds of reasoning we use only this part of the meaning of such statements. When used in this way, all seven statements have the same standard form: some boys are pupils on the honor roll. (*Some A are B.*) Here are some examples:

8) One boy is absent. *In standard form:* Some boys are pupils who are absent. (*Some A are B.*)

9) Almost all the girls have short hair. *In standard form:* Some girls are people with short hair. (*Some A are B.*)

10) Not all Italians are organ-grinders. *In standard form:* Some Italians are not organ-grinders. (*Some A are not B.*)

11) Not only Italians are organ-grinders. *In standard*

*form:* Some organ-grinders are not Italians. (*Some A are not B.*)

Rewrite each of these propositions in standard form, and state what the form is:

42. Two boys are eagle scouts.
43. Not all high school graduates go to college.
44. Girls like to play with dolls.
45. Not only men are elected to Congress.
46. No person is both a Democrat and a Republican.
47. If his parents have blue eyes, then he has blue eyes.
48. Anyone who wishes to may try out for the team.
49. Carpenters use hammers.
50. Most Americans live in cities.
51. There is nobody here except us chickens.

## Recognizing the Form

Rewrite each of these propositions in standard form, and draw the diagram that represents it:

52. Almost all the girls in the class are girl scouts.
53. If it is worth doing, it is worth doing well.
54. Not all people who wear trousers are men.
55. John hates school.

Write in standard form the proposition represented by each of these diagrams:

56.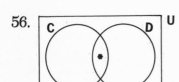

U = movies
C = cowboy movies
D = dull movies

57.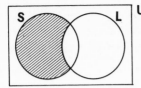

U = products
S = shoes
L = things made of leather

58.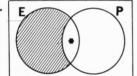

U = coins
B = British coins
R = round coins

59.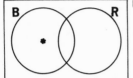

U = scientists
E = Einstein
P = physicists

60.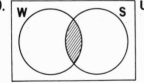

U = American people
W = women
S = Supreme Court judges

## How Many?

The words *all, some* and *no* (in the sense of none) used in propositions play an important part in them because they show how many members of a set we are talking about. Because they indicate a quantity, they are called quantifiers.

81

In each of the propositions below there is a blank space. Which of the quantifiers, *all, some,* or *no,* inserted into the blank space, will make the proposition a true statement? (In cases where the answer may be either *all* or *some,* give *all* as the answer.) Write your answers on a separate sheet of paper. Do not write in the book.

61. ... wood floats on water.
62. ... hurricanes start over water.
63. ... squares are not rectangles.
64. ... rabbits eat meat.
65. ... polygons are triangles.
66. ... streams flow uphill.
67. ... fish have backbones.
68. ... birds fly.
69. ... insects have six legs.
70. ... calendar years have 365 days.

CHAPTER VII

# *Relations*

## Relations and Terms

Some propositions assert that a relation connects certain members of a universe of discourse. The members that are connected by the relation are called the *terms* of the relation. For example, in the proposition "John is taller than Frank" *John* and *Frank* are the terms connected by the relation *is taller than*. Because it connects exactly two terms, the relation *is taller than* is called a two-term relation. In the proposition "New Hampshire is between Maine and Vermont," *New Hampshire, Maine,* and *Vermont* are the terms connected by the relation *is between*. Because it connects exactly three terms, the relation *is between* is called a three-term relation. In this chapter we consider only two-term relations. To get acquainted with some properties that relations may have, we shall examine the relations that occur in some very small universes of discourse.

## Three Things in a Line

We choose as our first universe of discourse a set of three things arranged in a line from left to right. In diagram I below the things are represented by dots and are labeled x, y, and z. A relation that connects

some members in this universe is the relation "is to the left of." This relation is asserted, for example, in the proposition, "x is to the left of y." Let us use the letter L as a symbol for the relation "is to the left of." Then the proposition "x is to the left of y" can be written in abbreviated form as "x L y." Notice that the two terms x and y are written in this proposition in a definite order: x is written first, and y is written second. If we reverse the order of the terms we get a different proposition, "y L x," that is, "y is to the left of x." In the universe of discourse shown in the diagram, the proposition "x L y" is true, but the proposition "y L x" is false. So we see that the order in which the terms is written is important. Whenever we assert that the relation L holds between two terms, it is not enough to identify the pair of terms. We must also specify the

84

*order* in which the terms are written by indicating which term is first and which term is second.

Let us list all the propositions we can write using the relation L and any two members of the universe of discourse. If we choose x as the first term, we may use either x or y or z as second term. This gives us three possible propositions, "x L x," "x L y," and "x L z." If we choose y as the first term, we may use either x or y or z as second term. This gives us three more possible propositions, "y L x," "y L y," and "y L z." If we choose z as the first term, we may use either x or y or z as second term. This gives us three more possible propositions, "z L x," "z L y," and "z L z." Altogether there are only nine possible propositions asserting that two members of the universe of discourse are connected by the relation L. Some of these propositions are true and some are false. To see which ones are true, all we have to do is look at diagram I. The table below lists all nine propositions, and indicates which are true and which are false.

| True | x L y, y L z, x L z |
|---|---|
| False | x L x, y L y, z L z, <br> y L x, z L y, z L x |

If we arrange the three things, x, y and z, in a different order, we get a different universe of discourse. For example, the universe of discourse in diagram II below is not the same as the universe shown in diagram I on page 84.

II    ●    ●    ●
     z    x    y

1. Write down all the possible properties that assert the relation L between members of the universe of discourse shown in diagram II. Arrange the propositions in a table indicating which ones are true and which are false.

## A Family of Four

We choose as our next universe of discourse a family of four people. The given information about this family is shown in the chart below. Each box represents a member of the family. The boxes on the upper line represent the parents, and the boxes on the lower line represent their children. In each box are listed the person's name, age, and eye color.

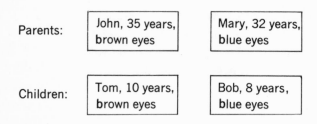

Let F stand for the relation "is the father of." There are sixteen different propositions that can be written, each asserting the relation F between members of this universe of discourse:

John F John, John F Mary, John F Tom, John F Bob,
Mary F John, Mary F Mary, Mary F Tom, Mary F Bob,
Tom F John, Tom F Mary, Tom F Tom, Tom F Bob,
Bob F John, Bob F Mary, Bob F Tom, Bob F Bob

Of these sixteen propositions, only two are true: John

F Tom, and John F Bob; that is, "John is the father of Tom" and "John is the father of Bob." All the other fourteen propositions are false.

Questions 2 to 6 refer to this family of four as universe of discourse:

2. Let H stand for the relation "is the husband of." List the sixteen different propositions that can be written, asserting the relation H between members of this universe of discourse. Underline those propositions that are true.

3. Let M stand for the relation "is married to." List the *true* propositions that can be written asserting the relation M between members of this universe.

4. Let B stand for the relation "is the brother of." List the *true* propositions that can be written asserting the relation B between members of this universe.

5. Let O stand for the relation "is older than." List the *true* propositions that can be written asserting the relation O between members of this universe.

6. Let C stand for the relation "has the same eye color as." List the *true* propositions that can be written asserting the relation C between members of this universe.

**Properties of Relations**

Among the answers to question 6 are the true propositions "John C John," "Mary C Mary," "Tom C Tom," and "Bob C Bob." That is, in the universe of discourse to which the relation C applies, the assertion that C joins any member of the universe to itself is a true proposition. Because of this property, we say that the relation C is *reflexive*. In general, a relation R is reflexive if, for every member x of the universe of discourse, the proposition "x R x" is true.

Notice that "John M John" is not among the answers to question 3, because it is not true that John is married to John. So the relation M ("is married to") is not reflexive.

7. Is the relation H, as defined in question 2, reflexive?
8. Is the relation B, as defined in question 4, reflexive?
9. Is the relation O, as defined in question 5, reflexive?
10. In the universe of discourse consisting of all people, let W stand for the relation "has the same weight as." Is the relation W reflexive?

The answers to question 3 are the true propositions "John M Mary" and "Mary M John." If we take any one of these true propositions and interchange the terms that are joined by M, the result is another true proposition. For example, if we interchange the terms *John* and *Mary* in the true proposition "John M Mary," the result is the true proposition "Mary M John." Because of this property we say that the relation M is *symmetrical*. In general, a relation R is symmetrical if, for every true proposition "x R y," the proposition "y R x" is also true.

Notice that the relation H defined in question 2 is not symmetrical because, although the proposition "John is the husband of Mary" is true, the proposition "Mary is the husband of John" is not true.

11. Is the relation B, as defined in question 4, symmetrical?

12. Is the relation O, as defined in question 5, symmetrical?

13. Is the relation C, as defined in question 6, symmetrical?

The answers to question 5 include the true propositions "John O Mary" and "Mary O Tom." Notice that the proposition "John O Tom" is also true. This is an example of the following property of the relation O ("is older than"): If the first of three people is older than the second, and the second is older than the third, then the first is older than the third. Because of this property, we say that the relation O is *transitive*. In general, a relation R is transitive if, whenever "x R y" and "y R z" are true propositions, then "x R z" is also a true proposition.

Notice that the relation F ("is the father of") is not transitive, because if x is the father of y and y is the father of z, then it is not true that x is the father of z. In fact, x would be a grandfather of z.

14. Is the relation C, as defined in question 6, transitive?

15. Is the relation M, as defined in question 3, transitive?

16. Is the relation B, as defined in question 4, transitive?

17. Let A, B and C be sets in some universe of discourse. If the propositions, "A is a subset of B," and "B is a subset of C" are both true, is the proposition "A is a subset of C" also true? Is the relation "is a subset of" transitive?

## CHAPTER VIII

# Related Propositions

## Building a Universe

Suppose we set out to build a miniature universe of discourse consisting of three things, x, y, and z, arranged in a horizontal line. We saw on page 85 that there are nine possible propositions asserting the relation L (is to the left of) in such a universe. Let us see how much free choice we have in deciding which of these propositions shall be made true by the way in which we build the universe.

We note first that there is no way of arranging the three things, x, y and z, so that x L x, or y L y, or z L z. That is, no object can be to the left of itself. So we cannot choose to make any of the three propositions, x L x, y L y, or z L z true. This leaves only six propositions where there may be any free choice at all: x L y, x L z, y L z, y L x, z L x, and z L y. There is some real freedom of choice here. Consider, for example, the proposition x L y. We may choose to make this proposition either true or false. To make it true, all we need do is put x to the left of y: To make it false, all we need do is put x to the right of y. Suppose we choose to put x to the left of y, so that the proposition x L y is made true. Then our partially completed universe looks like this:

To complete the universe we have to choose the place in line where we shall put z. Notice that there are really only three places where z may be put. We may put it to the left of x, or between x and y, or to the right of y. Suppose we choose to place z in such a way as to make the proposition z L x true. Then we place z to the left of x, as shown in the diagram below.

The universe is now complete. We brought it to completion by choosing to make the propositions x L y and z L x true propositions. But since the universe is now complete, we can no longer freely choose to make other propositions true or false. We are not free, for example, to choose to make the proposition z L y false.

The diagram shows that in this universe the proposition z L y must be true. Similarly, we are not free to choose to make any of the propositions x L z, y L x, or y L z true. The diagram shows that in this universe these three propositions must be false.

What we have shown is that some of the propositions about a universe of discourse are *related* to each other. The propositions x L y and y L x are related in such a way that they cannot both be true. If one of them is true, then the other is false. This relation is called *contradiction*, and we say that the proposition x L y *contradicts* the proposition y L x. The propositions z L x, x L y and z L y are related in such a way that if the first two propositions are true, then the third one must also be true. This relation is called *implication*, and we say that z L x and x L y together *imply* z L y. The implication in this case is the result of the fact that the relation L is transitive.

**Arguments**

The fact that some propositions imply others is the basis for the third method of obtaining knowledge (see page 10), the method of reasoning. For example, if we know from observation that z is to the left of x, and x is to the left of y, then we can conclude by reasoning that z is to the left of y. The reasoning consists of a chain of propositions in which some propositions known to be true are used to prove that another proposition is also true. Such a chain of propositions is called an *argument*. The proposition that the argument aims to prove is called the *conclusion* of the argument. The propositions used to prove the conclusion are called the *reasons* for it.

There are certain key words that we generally use when we present an argument. They are words such as *if, then, therefore, that is why,* and *because.* The positions of these words in the argument help us to identify the conclusion and the reasons in the argument. For example, we might say, "If z is to the left of x, and x is to the left of y, then z is to the left of y." Notice that the word *if* introduces the reasons, while the word *then* introduces the conclusion. Sometimes the word *then* is omitted, but it is understood to be there. We might also present the argument in the form of three statements as follows: "z is to the left of x; x is to the left of y; therefore z is to the left of y." When the argument is in this form, the word *therefore* introduces the conclusion and is preceded by the reasons. The expression *that is why* is sometimes used in the same way in the place of the word *therefore.* In another form in which the argument is sometimes cast, no special word is used to introduce the conclusion, but the word *because* is used to introduce the reasons, thus: z is to the left of y because z is to the left of x, and x is to the left of y. To simplify our discussion of arguments, we shall use only the form in which the reasons are stated first, and the conclusion is then introduced by the word *therefore.*

## Arguments that Prove Nothing

There are some arguments that really do not prove their conclusions. For example, someone may make the argument, "John likes school. John is a boy. Therefore all boys like school." Even if the two reasons given in this argument are true, they do not guarantee that the conclusion is also true. So it is necessary to distinguish between an argument that really proves its conclusion and an argument that does not. An argument that really proves its conclusion is called a *valid* argument. An argument that does not really prove its conclusion is called an *invalid* argument. Notice that the words *valid* and *invalid* describe possible qualities of an argument, while the words *true* and *false* describe possible qualities of a proposition.

### Syllogisms

On page 78 we listed six different kinds of simple propositions written in standard form. Each simple proposition makes an assertion about two sets, or about an individual and a set. The two sets, or the individual and the set, are called the *terms* of the proposition. For example, in the proposition "all squares are rectangles," the terms are *squares* and *rectangles*. In the proposition "John is a boy," the terms are *John* and *boys*.

A very important type of argument that is often used is one that has these two characteristics:
1) It is a chain of three simple propositions. One of the propositions is the conclusion of the argument. The other two propositions are the reasons.
2) There are three terms in the whole argument. Each term appears exactly twice in the argument, but no more than once in any proposition in the argument.
An argument that has these two characteristics is called

a *syllogism*. The reasons in a syllogism are usually called the *premises* of the syllogism.

## A Valid Syllogism

Consider the following syllogism. *All squares are rectangles. All rectangles are quadrilaterals. Therefore all squares are quadrilaterals.* In this syllogism, the propositions "all squares are rectangles" and "all rectangles are quadrilaterals" are the premises. The proposition "all squares are quadrilaterals" is the conclusion.

We can find out if this syllogism is a valid argument by using a diagram. Let the universe of discourse U be the set of plane figures. We begin the diagram by drawing three overlapping circles, S, R, and Q, one for each of the terms in the syllogism, as follows:

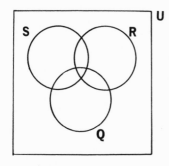

U = plane figures
S = squares
R = rectangles
Q = quadrilaterals

In Chapter VI we learned how to draw a diagram for any simple proposition. To show the proposition "all squares are rectangles," we shade that part of the circle S that is not inside the circle R:

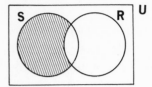

U = plane figures
S = squares
R = rectangles

To show the proposition "all rectangles are quadrilaterals," we shade that part of the circle R that is not inside the circle Q:

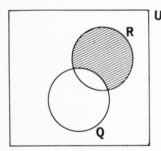

U = plane figures
R = rectangles
Q = quadrilaterals

However, instead of making two separate diagrams for the premises, we combine the two diagrams into one by doing the shading in the diagram that contains all three circles, S, R, and Q. The completed diagram looks like this:

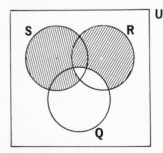

U = plane figures
S = squares
R = rectangles
Q = quadrilaterals

To find out if the syllogism is valid we look at this diagram to see if it also contains the diagram of the conclusion. Since the conclusion contains the terms "squares" and "quadrilaterals," we look at the circles S and Q, and disregard the circle R. Notice that the part of the circle S that is not inside the circle Q is completely shaded. But when the part of the circle S that is not inside the circle Q is shaded, the diagram represents the proposition "all squares are quadrilaterals," which is the conclusion of the syllogism. Thus the diagram for the two premises of the syllogism automatically produces the diagram for the conclusion of the syllogism. Because of this fact, we know that if the premises are true the conclusion must be true, and the syllogism is valid.

The syllogism we have just examined has the form: "all S are R; all R are Q; therefore all S are Q." Any syllogism that has this form has the diagram we have just examined. So any syllogism that has this form is valid. For example, consider the syllogism "all boys are girls; all girls are rabbits; therefore all boys are rabbits." If we let S stand for boys, let R stand for girls, and let Q stand for rabbits, we see that the syllogism has the form "all S are R; all R are Q; therefore all S are Q." Therefore the syllogism has the diagram shown on page 96, and the syllogism is valid.

It may seem strange that a valid argument may contain false premises like "all boys are girls" and a false conclusion like "all boys are rabbits." However, it is really not so strange when we remember that a syllogism doesn't assert that its conclusion is true. It merely asserts that the conclusion *would be* true *if* the premises were true. To find out if a syllogism is valid, it is not necessary to pay attention to the truth or falsity of its premises or conclusions. Just examine the form of the syllogism, as represented by a diagram. *If the combined diagram for the premises automatically produces the diagram for the conclusion, the syllogism is valid.*

### An Invalid Syllogism

Consider the syllogism "all cats are animals; no dogs are cats; therefore no dogs are animals." In this syllogism, both premises are true, and the conclusion is false. In a valid syllogism, if the premises are true, the conclusion must also be true. So this syllogism is obviously invalid. Let us see how we can discover that the syllogism is invalid by merely examining its form as shown by a diagram.

We begin the diagram by drawing three overlapping circles, C, A, and D, to represent cats, animals, and dogs, respectively. To show the proposition "all cats are animals," we shade that part of C that is not inside A. To show the proposition "no dogs are cats," we shade that part of D that is inside C. The completed diagram looks like this:

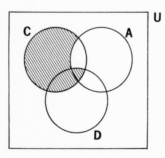

U = living things
C = cats
A = animals
D = dogs

To see if the syllogism is valid, we look at the completed diagram to see if it contains the diagram for the proposition "no dogs are animals." The diagram for this proposition consists of the circles D and A with that part of D that is inside A completely shaded. However, in the diagram for the syllogism, the part of D that is inside A is *not* completely shaded. Since the combined diagram of the premises does not automatically produce the diagram of the conclusion, the syllogism is invalid.

## Testing a Syllogism

To find out if a syllogism is valid or invalid, draw a combined diagram of its two premises. If the combined diagram of the premises automatically produces the diagram of the conclusion, the syllogism is valid. If it does not, the syllogism is invalid. To show how this test may be applied to different kinds of syllogisms, we examine some additional examples below.

In the diagram we draw for each syllogism there will be three overlapping circles, one for each term in the syllogism. Each circle is divided into several parts. To make it easy to refer to these parts we shall number them, as in the diagram below. The numbers will not be inserted in the separate diagram we draw for each example. If you do not remember what part a number refers to, look at this diagram again.

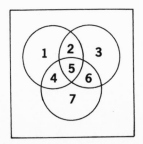

*Example 1.* All dogs are animals. No animal is a plant. Therefore no dog is a plant.

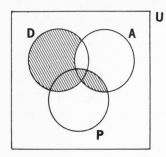

U = living things
D = dogs
A = animals
P = plants

To show the premise "all dogs are animals," shade parts 1 and 4. To show the premise "no animal is a plant," shade parts 5 and 6. The conclusion "no dog is a plant" is shown if parts 4 and 5 are shaded. Since parts 4 and 5 already *are* shaded, we see that the combined diagram for the premises automatically produces the diagram for the conclusion. Therefore this syllogism is valid.

*Example 2.* All children go to school. Some actors are children. Therefore some actors go to school.

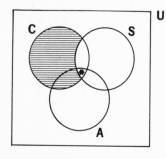

U = people
C = children
S = people who go to school
A = actors

When one of the premises begins with the word *some*, while the other one begins with the word *all*, first draw the diagram for the premise that begins with the word *all*. To show the premise "all children go to school," shade parts 1 and 4. To show the premise "some actors are children," we have to put an asterisk into the intersection of A and C. This intersection consists of the two parts numbered 4 and 5. So the asterisk has to be in either 4 or 5. However, part 4 is already shaded, showing that it is supposed to be empty. So we have to put the asterisk into part 5. The conclusion "some actors go to school" is shown if there is an asterisk in the intersection of A and S. This intersection consists of parts 5 and 6. Since there *is* an asterisk in part 5, we see that the combined diagram for the premises automatically produces the diagram for the conclusion. Therefore this syllogism is valid.

*Example 3.* No chickens are four-legged. Some birds are chickens. Therefore some birds are not four-legged.

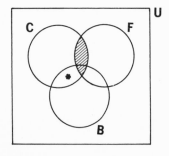

U = animals
C = chickens
F = four-legged animals
B = birds

When one of the premises begins with the word *some*, while the other one begins with the word *no*, first draw the diagram for the premise that begins with the word *no*. To show the premise "no chickens are four-legged," shade parts 2 and 5. To show the premise "some birds are chickens," we have to put an asterisk into the intersection of B and C. This intersection consists of the two parts numbered 4 and 5. So the asterisk has to be in either 4 or 5. However, part 5 is already shaded, showing that it is supposed to be empty. So we have to put the asterisk into part 4. The conclusion "some birds are not four-legged" is shown if there is an asterisk in the part of B that is not inside F. This part consists of parts 4 and 7. Since there *is* an asterisk in part 4, we see that the combined diagram for the premises automatically produces the diagram for the conclusion. Therefore this syllogism is valid.

*Example 4.* John is a boy. All boys play baseball. Therefore John plays baseball.

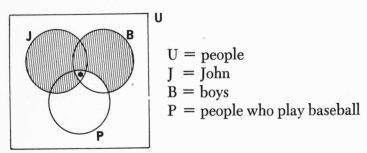

U = people
J = John
B = boys
P = people who play baseball

When one of the premises concerns an individual, while the other one begins with the word *all*, first draw the diagram for the premise that begins with the word *all*. To show the premise "all boys play baseball," shade parts 2 and 3. To show the premise "John is a boy," shade parts 1 and 4, and put an asterisk into the intersection of J and B. This intersection consists of the two parts numbered 2 and 5. So the asterisk has to be in either 2 or 5. However, part 2 is already shaded, showing that it is supposed to be empty. So we have to put the asterisk into part 5. The conclusion "John plays baseball" is shown if parts 1 and 2 are shaded and there is an asterisk in either 4 or 5. Since parts 1 and 2 *are* shaded, and there *is* an asterisk in part 5, we see that the combined diagram for the premises automatically produces the diagram for the conclusion. Therefore this syllogism is valid.

*Example 5.* All girls are human. All humans are two-legged animals. Therefore all two-legged animals are girls.

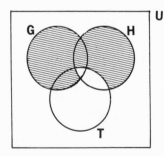

U = animals
G = girls
H = humans
T = two-legged animals

To show the premise "all girls are human," shade parts 1 and 4. To show the premise "all humans are two-legged animals," shade parts 2 and 3. The conclusion "all two-legged animals are girls" is shown if parts 6 and 7 are shaded. Since parts 6 and 7 are *not* shaded, we see that the combined diagram for the premises does *not* automatically produce the diagram for the conclusion. Therefore this syllogism is invalid.

*Example 6.* All alligators are reptiles. Some vertebrates are not reptiles. Therefore some vertebrates are alligators.

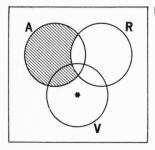

U = animals
A = alligators
R = reptiles
V = vertebrates

To show the premise "all alligators are reptiles," shade parts 1 and 4. To show the premise "some vertebrates are not reptiles," we have to put an asterisk into the part of V that is not inside R. This part consists of the two parts numbered 4 and 7. So the asterisk has to be in either 4 or 7. However, part 4 is already shaded, showing that it is supposed to be empty. So we have to put the asterisk into part 7. The conclusion "some vertebrates are alligators" is shown if there is an asterisk in either part 5 or part 6. Since there is no asterisk in 5 or 6, we see that the combined diagram for the premises does *not* automatically produce the diagram for the conclusion. Therefore this syllogism is invalid.

Notice that the syllogism is invalid even though the three propositions in it are all true. This means that while the conclusion happens to be true, the premises do not *prove* that it is true.

*Example* 7. All cats are furry. Some cats are not striped. Therefore some striped animals are not furry.

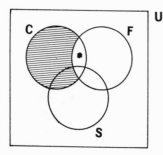

U = animals
C = cats
F = furry animals
S = striped animals

To show the premise "all cats are furry," shade parts 1 and 4. To show the premise "some cats are not striped," we have to put an asterisk in the part of C that is not inside S. This part consists of the two parts numbered 1 and 2. So the asterisk has to be in either 1 or 2. But part 1 is already shaded, showing that it is supposed to be empty. So we have to put the asterisk into part 2. The conclusion "some striped animals are not furry" is shown if there is an asterisk in either part 4 or part 7. Since there is no asterisk in 4 or 7, we see that the combined diagram for the premises does *not* automatically produce the diagram for the conclusion. Therefore this syllogism is invalid.

*Example 8.* All trout are fish. All fish live in water. Therefore some water animals are not trout.

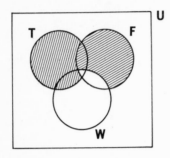

U = animals
T = trout
F = fish
W = water animals

To show the premise "all trout are fish," shade parts 1 and 4. To show the premise "all fish live in water," shade parts 2 and 3. The conclusion "some water animals are not trout" is shown if there is an asterisk in either part 6 or part 7. Since there is no asterisk in 6 or 7, we see that the combined diagram for the premises does *not* automatically produce the diagram for the conclusion. Therefore this syllogism is invalid.

*Example 9.* All Italians are Europeans. Some Europeans are Catholics. Therefore some Catholics are Italians.

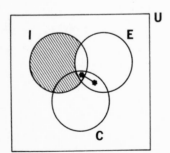

U = people
I = Italians
E = Europeans
C = Catholics

To show the premise "all Italians are Europeans," shade parts 1 and 4. To show the premise "some Europeans are Catholics," we have to put an asterisk into the intersection of E and C. This intersection consists of the two parts numbered 5 and 6. So the asterisk has to be in either 5 or 6. Neither 5 nor 6 is shaded. So we do not know whether the asterisk is supposed to be in 5 or in 6. To show that it may be in either 5 or 6, put an asterisk in each of them and join the asterisks with a line. The two asterisks joined by a line are our way of showing in the diagram that we do not have enough information to be sure of exactly where the asterisk belongs. The conclusion "some Catholics are Italians" is shown if there is an asterisk in either part 4 or part 5. There is no asterisk in part 4, and we are not sure if there is an asterisk in part 5. So we see that the combined diagram for the premises does *not* automatically produce the diagram for the conclusion. Therefore this syllogism is invalid.

*Example 10.* All nails are made of metal. Some metal things are not iron. Therefore some nails are not iron.

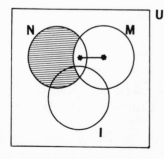

U = hardware
N = nails
M = metal things
I = iron things

To show the premise "all nails are made of metal," shade parts 1 and 4. To show the premise "some metal things are not iron," we have to put an asterisk into the part of M that is not inside I. This part consists of the two numbered parts 2 and 3. We do not know whether the asterisk belongs in 2 or 3, so we show our uncertainty by putting an asterisk into each of them, and joining the asterisks with a line. The conclusion "some nails are not iron" is shown if there is an asterisk in either 1 or 2. There is no asterisk in 1, and we are not sure if there is an asterisk in 2. So we see that the combined diagram for the premise does *not* automatically produce the diagram for the conclusion. Therefore this syllogism is invalid.

*Example 11.* No Vermonter is a spendthrift. Jones is a Vermonter. Therefore Jones is not a spendthrift.

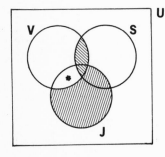

U = people
V = Vermonters
S = spendthrifts
J = Jones

To show the premise "no Vermonter is a spendthrift," shade parts 2 and 5. To show the premise "Jones is a Vermonter," we have to shade the part of J that is not inside V, and we have to put an asterisk into the inter-

108

section of J and V. The part of J that is not inside V consists of parts 6 and 7, so we shade parts 6 and 7. The intersection of J and V consists of parts 4 and 5. So the asterisk has to be in either 4 or 5. But part 5 is already shaded, showing that it is supposed to be empty. So we have to put the asterisk into part 4. The conclusion "Jones is not a spendthrift" is shown if parts 5 and 6 are shaded and there is an asterisk in either part 4 or part 7. Parts 5 and 6 *are* shaded, and there *is* an asterisk in part 4, so we see that the combined diagram for the premises automatically produces the diagram for the conclusion. Therefore this syllogism is valid.

*Example 12.* Shakespeare is a playwright. Some playwrights are poets. Therefore Shakespeare is a poet.

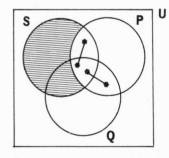

U = writers
S = Shakespeare
P = playwrights
Q = poets

To show the premise "Shakespeare is a playwright," we have to shade the part of S that is not inside P, and we have to put an asterisk into the intersection of S and P. The part of S that is not inside P consists of parts

1 and 4, so we shade parts 1 and 4. The intersection of S and P consists of parts 2 and 5. We do not know whether the asterisk belongs in 2 or 5, so we show our uncertainty by putting an asterisk into each of them, and joining the asterisks with a line. To show the premise "some playwrights are poets," we have to put an asterisk into the intersection of P and Q. This intersection consists of parts 5 and 6. We do not know whether the asterisk belongs in 5 or 6, so we show our uncertainty by putting an asterisk into each of them, and joining the asterisks with a line. The conclusion "Shakespeare is a poet" is shown if parts 1 and 2 are shaded, and there is an asterisk in either part 4 or part 5. But part 2 is not shaded, there is no asterisk in part 4, and we are not sure if there is an asterisk in part 5. So we see that the combined diagram for the premises does not automatically produce the diagram for the conclusion. Therefore this syllogism is invalid.

*Example 13.* Frank is human. No Martians are human. Therefore Frank is not a Martian.

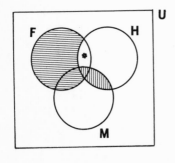

U = living things
F = Frank
H = human beings
M = Martians

When one of the premises concerns an individual, while the other one begins with the word *no,* first draw the diagram for the premise that begins with the word *no.* To show the premise "no Martians are human," shade parts 5 and 6. To show the premise "Frank is human," we have to shade parts 1 and 4, and put an asterisk into the intersection of F and H. The intersection of F and H consists of parts 2 and 5. Part 5 is already shaded, showing that it is supposed to be empty. So we have to put the asterisk into part 2. The conclusion "Frank is not a Martian" is shown if parts 4 and 5 are shaded and there is an asterisk in either part 1 or part 2. Since parts 4 and 5 *are* shaded, and there *is* an asterisk in part 2, we see that the combined diagram for the premises automatically produces the diagram for the conclusion. Therefore this syllogism is valid.

*Example 14.* All A are B. Some C are not B. Therefore some C are not A.

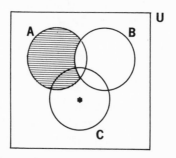

To show the premise "all A are B," shade parts 1 and 4. To show the premise "some C are not B," we have to put an asterisk into that part of C that is not inside B.

This part consists of parts 4 and 7. Part 4 is already shaded, showing that is is supposed to be empty. So we have to put the asterisk into part 7. The conclusion "some C are not A" is shown if there is an asterisk in either part 7 or part 6. Since there is an asterisk in part 6, we see that the combined diagram for the premises automatically produces the diagram for the conclusion. Therefore this syllogism is valid.

*Example 15.* No A are B. No A are C. Therefore all C are B.

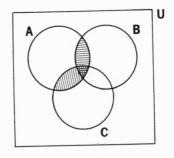

To show the premise "no A are B," shade parts 2 and 5. To show the premise "no A are C," shade parts 4 and 5. The conclusion "all C are B" is shown if parts 4 and 7 are shaded. Since part 7 is *not* shaded, we see that the combined diagram for the premises does *not* automatically produce the diagram for the conclusion. Therefore this syllogism is invalid.

112

*Example 16.* Some A are B. No C are A. Therefore some C are not B.

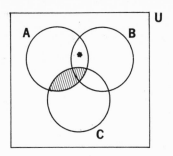

To show the premise "no C are A," shade parts 4 and 5. To show the premise "some A are B," we have to put an asterisk into the intersection of A and B. This intersection consists of parts 2 and 5. Part 5 is already shaded, showing that it is supposed to be empty. So we have to put the asterisk into part 2. The conclusion "some C are not B" is shown if there is an asterisk in either part 4 or part 7. Since there is no asterisk in 4 or 7, we see that the combined diagram for the premises does *not* automatically produce the diagram for the conclusion. Therefore this syllogism is invalid.

For each of the following syllogisms, draw a combined diagram for the two premises, and state whether the syllogism is valid or invalid:

1. All ants are insects. All insects are six-legged. Therefore all six-legged animals are ants.
2. All misers are stingy. No stingy people are generous. Therefore no misers are generous.

3. Mrs. Hag is a witch. All witches are broom riders. Therefore Mrs. Hag is a broom rider.
4. All butterflies have wings. Some insects are butterflies. Therefore some insects have wings.
5. All birds are two-legged. Some two-legged animals are swimmers. Therefore some swimmers are birds.
6. No aliens are voters. Mr. French is an alien. Therefore Mr. French is not a voter.
7. No trees walk. Some plants are trees. Therefore some plants do not walk.
8. All A are B. Some C are not B. Therefore some C are A.
9. All A are B. Some B are not C. Therefore some A are not C.
10. All crows fly. Some birds do not fly. Therefore some birds are not crows.

## Draw Your Own Conclusion

In example 6 on page 104 we examined the following syllogism: "All alligators are reptiles. Some vertebrates are not reptiles. Therefore some vertebrates are alligators." We found that this syllogism is invalid. That is, the conclusion of the syllogism is not proved by the premises. Let us throw away this conclusion, then, and see if we can find some other conclusion that *is* proved by the premises. The two premises are: 1) All alligators are reptiles. 2) Some vertebrates are not reptiles. The terms that appear in these premises are *alligators, reptiles,* and *vertebrates.* The term *alligators* appears once in the premises. The term *reptiles* appears twice. The term *vertebrates* appears once. In a complete syllogism each of the three terms appears exactly twice. So we know that in order to complete the syllogism we need a conclusion that contains the terms *alligators* and *vertebrates*. To find a conclusion that will make the syllogism valid we examine the combined diagram for the premises. This diagram, already drawn on page 104, is repeated below.

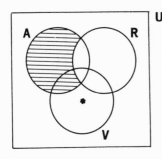

U = animals
A = alligators
R = reptiles
V = vertebrates

Since the conclusion must contain the terms *alligators* and *vertebrates*, we examine the circles A and V. By seeing whether any parts of these circles are shaded, and whether any part contains an asterisk, we can find out if the diagram made up of these two circles represents any proposition. If it does, that proposition is a conclusion that is proved by the premises. In this case we see an asterisk in that part of V that is not inside A. So the conclusion that can be drawn from the premises is, "Some vertebrates are not alligators."

To show clearly how you can draw your own conclusion from two premises we give some additional examples:

*Example 1.* What conclusion, if any, can be drawn from the premises "all natives are citizens; some natives are not voters"? The combined diagram for the premises looks like this:

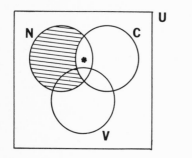

U = people
N = natives
C = citizens
V = voters

In the premises, the term *natives* occurs twice, the term *citizens* occurs once, and the term *voters* occurs once. So the conclusion must contain the terms *citizens* and *voters*. Therefore we look for the diagram of a proposition in circles C and V. There is an asterisk in that part of C that is not inside V. So the conclusion is, "Some citizens are not voters."

*Example 2.* What conclusion, if any, can be drawn from the premises, "all A are B; all B are C"? The combined diagram for the premises looks like this:

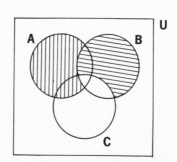

In the premises, the term A occurs once, the term B occurs twice, and the term C occurs once. So the conclusion must contain the terms A and C. Therefore we look for the diagram of a proposition in the circles A and C. The part of A that is not inside C is shaded. So the conclusion is, "All A are C."

*Example 3.* What conclusion, if any, can be drawn from the premises "no man is a witch; Mr. Jones is a man"? The combined diagram for the premises looks like this:

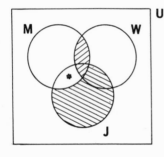

U = people
M = men
W = witches
J  = Mr. Jones

In the premises, the term *man* occurs twice, the term *witch* occurs once, and the term *Mr. Jones* occurs once. So the conclusion must contain the terms *witch* and *Mr. Jones*. Therefore we look for the diagram of a proposition in the circles W and J. The intersection of W and J is shaded, and there is an asterisk in the part of J that is not inside W. So the conclusion is, "Mr. Jones is not a witch."

117

*Example 4.* What conclusion, if any, can be drawn from the premises "all A are B; some B are not C"? The combined diagram for the premises looks like this:

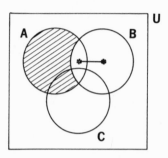

In the premises, the term A occurs once, the term B occurs twice, and the term C occurs once. So the conclusion must contain the terms A and C. Therefore we look for the diagram of a proposition in the circles A and C. The part of A that is inside C is not completely shaded, so the diagram does not represent the proposition "all A are not C." The part of A that is not inside C is not completely shaded, so the diagram does not represent the proposition "all A are C." Although we see an asterisk in the part of A that is not inside C, it is joined to another asterisk. This means that we are not sure where the asterisk really is. So the diagram does not represent the proposition "some A are not C." In fact, the diagram does not represent any simple proposition about A and C. Therefore we cannot draw any conclusion at all from the given premises.

118

Each of the following exercises lists two premises. Draw the combined diagram for the premises and state what conclusion, if any, is proved by these premises.

11. No cats have horns. Some mammals are cats.
12. All goops are wowsies. Some serps are goops.
13. All squares are quadrilaterals. All quadrilaterals are polygons.
14. No gentlemen are liars. Mr. Brown is a gentleman.
15. All squirrels are rodents. No rodent is a fish.
16. All ducks are birds. Some vertebrates are not birds.
17. No A are B. No A are C.
18. Some men are ugly. No women are men.
19. X is an A. All A are B.
20. Dr. Gauss is a mathematician. No pygmies are mathematicians.

## Generalizing

On page 102 we found that the following argument is valid: "John is a boy. All boys play baseball. Therefore John plays baseball." In this argument, from a premise about all the members of the set of people called *boys* ("all boys play baseball"), we draw a conclusion about one of the members of the set ("John plays baseball"). A different kind of argument that reverses the procedure is obtained if we interchange this premise and conclusion. Then the argument says, "John is a boy. John plays baseball. Therefore all boys play baseball." In this argument, from a premise about one member of a set we draw a conclusion about all members of the set. This kind of argument is known as *generalizing from a single example.* Some people often use this kind of argument. They shouldn't, however, because the argument is invalid.

One way of seeing that it is invalid is to draw the combined diagram for the two premises. In the diagram below, to show the premise "John is a boy," we

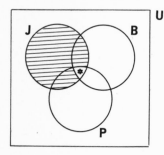

U = people
J = John
B = boys
P = people who play baseball

shade parts 1 and 4, and we have to put an asterisk into 2 or 5. Before putting in the asterisk, let us try to show the premise "John plays baseball." To show this premise, we shade parts 1 and 2, and we have to put an asterisk into 4 or 5. So there is supposed to be an asterisk in 2, or 4 or 5. But parts 2 and 4 are both shaded, showing that they are empty. Therefore the asterisk must be in part 5. Since part 3 is *not* shaded, we cannot draw the conclusion "all boys play baseball." However, since there is an asterisk in the intersection of B and P. we can draw the conclusion "some boys play baseball."

**Proving or Disproving a Rule**

To see in another way why it is wrong to generalize from a single example, let us consider the following problem. Suppose an urn A contains five balls, one of which is black and four of which are white. Suppose that John, who does not know the contents of the urn, decides to find out what they are by drawing a ball from the urn. He draws out one ball, sees that it is black, and he comes to the conclusion that all the balls in the urn are black. His reasoning is obviously invalid, because knowing the color of one ball gives him no information about the color of the other balls. Without examining all the other balls in the urn, he cannot tell whether the black ball is typical, as in urn C, or is exceptional, as in urn A. *A single example does not prove a rule.*

If a single example is not enough to prove a rule, how many examples *do* we need to prove a rule about all members of a set? To answer this question, let us imagine that John draws four balls from urn B, and finds that all four are black. If he concludes that all the balls in urn B are black, his reasoning is still invalid, because the one ball that he did not draw may not be black. If you want to prove a rule about members of a set by examining individual members of the set, you must examine *every* member of the set. If you fail to examine a single member of the set the rule is not proved.

Although a single example cannot prove a rule, *a single example can disprove a rule*. For example, if a single white ball is drawn from an urn, then we know that the proposition "all the balls in the urn are black" is false.

Which of these general statements are true and which are false? If the statement is false, give an example that proves it is false. (Do not write your answers in the book.)

21. All squares have four sides.
22. All past Presidents of the United States were Protestants.
23. All the states of the United States are in North America.
24. All the radii of a circle are equal to each other.
25. All wars fought by the United States were fought on foreign soil.

# The Game of "As If"

## The Closed Box

The diagram below represents a box that is completely closed except for two tiny holes at the bottom. Two equal weights, A and B, are hanging from ropes threaded through these holes. *Suppose that each of the weights A or B can be pulled down, and that, when one weight is pulled down any distance, the other weight moves up an equal distance.* The object of the game is to explain why this happens, without opening

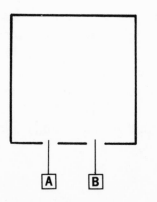

the box to see what is inside. To explain the behavior of the weights we try to imagine a hookup of ropes and pulleys inside the box that would make the weights behave the way they do. Then we can say the weights behave *as if* there were such and such a hookup inside the box. There are many possible solutions to this game of "as if." One of them is shown in the drawing below:

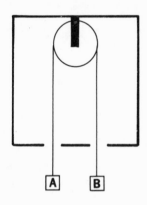

1. Suppose that, *when A is pulled down any distance, B moves up twice that distance.* Draw a hookup of ropes and pulleys that would explain this behavior of the weights.
2. Suppose that, *when B is pulled down any distance, A moves up three times that distance.* Draw a hookup of ropes and pulleys that would explain this behavior of the weights.
3. Suppose that, *when B is pulled down any distance, A moves down twice that distance.* Draw a hookup of ropes and pulleys that would explain this behavior of the weights.

## The Periscope

A periscope is a device by which you can see in one direction by looking in another direction. Each of the boxes below represents a different kind of periscope. The eye looks into the box through one hole, and sees things outside the box through the other hole, in the direction indicated by the arrow. In each case draw an arrangement of mirrors inside the box that would explain why the box behaves the way it does.

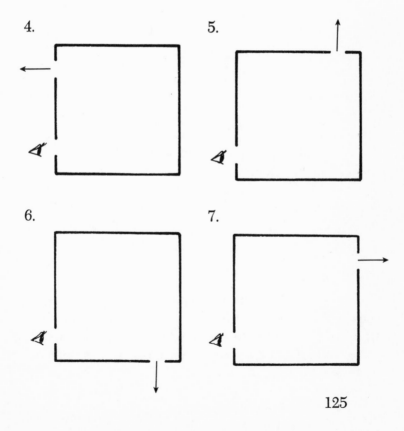

4.

5.

6.

7.

## "Droodles"

A popular game consists of showing someone a drawing made of a few simple lines and asking him what it is a picture of. The drawing below is a typical example. The expected answer is, "a soldier and a dog going around a corner." The game is really a variety of the

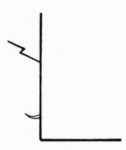

"as if" game, because the answer means, "it looks *as if* a soldier and a dog have just gone around a corner, and we see the bayonet of the soldier and the tail of the dog just before they disappear from view." The cartoonist Roger Price called drawings like these *droodles*. Some droodles are shown on page 127. See if you can tell what each "droodle" is a picture of.

## "As if" in Daily Life

The game of "as if" is not merely a game. It is an important method of thinking that we use all the time in our daily lives. We use it whenever we see something and try to figure out what must have happened to bring about what we see.

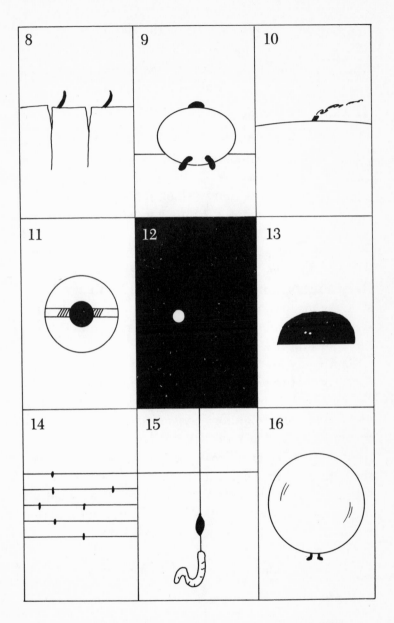

A scene is shown in each of the drawings on page 129. Express your judgment of what caused the scene by completing the sentence "It looks as if . . ." (Write your answers on a separate sheet of paper.)

**Making Up Reasons**

The game of "as if" is the opposite of the game "draw your own conclusion." In the game "draw your own conclusion," as we played it on page 114, we are given some *reasons*, and we look for a *conclusion* that follows from the reasons. In the game of "as if," we are given a *conclusion* consisting of the scene or events that we observe, and we try to make up *reasons* that will explain the *conclusion*. For example, to explain why the man shown in drawing number 17 on page 129 is so wet, we may make up these reasons: It is raining outside. The man was caught in the rain, and did not have an umbrella.

Somebody else looking at drawing number 17 may make up entirely different reasons to explain why the man is wet. He may say, for example, that the man is wet because his neighbor was watering his garden, and, turning the garden hose without looking, he accidentally poured water all over him. Both sets of reasons serve to explain what we see in the drawing. Which set of reasons is correct? We cannot tell from what we see in the drawing alone. We need more information before we can reject one or the other set of reasons as being wrong.

A set of reasons used to explain a given set of facts

128

is called a *hypothesis*. When a detective tries to solve a crime, first he gathers all the facts that he can that relate to the crime. These are his "clues." Then he makes up several hypotheses, each of which could explain the facts. Then he sets out to eliminate some of the hypotheses. To eliminate some of these hypotheses he follows this procedure: First he draws as many conclusions as he can from each hypothesis. Second he looks for new facts that will either agree with or contradict these new conclusions. If the new facts contradict any conclusions drawn from a hypothesis, then the hypothesis is false, and it must be rejected. If the new facts agree with conclusions drawn from the hypothesis, then they are additional evidence in favor of that hypothesis. If the detective starts with three hypotheses and he proves two of them are false, he is still not sure that the third one is true. But at least he knows that it is the only one that *may* be true. He hopes that, as he continues his investigation, he will turn up some facts that will prove beyond doubt that the third hypothesis really is true.

## Hypotheses in Science

The work of a scientist is like the work of a detective trying to solve a crime. The result of an experiment is the "crime" that the scientist is trying to solve. The measurements he makes in the experiment are his "clues." The scientist makes up a hypothesis, which is a set of reasons that can explain what happened in the experiment. The scientist next draws additional conclusions from the hypothesis. These new conclusions

130

are called "predictions." Then he performs new experiments to see if the predictions are true. If the predictions made from a hypothesis turn out to be false, then the hypothesis is false. If the predictions turn out to be true, they are additional evidence in favor of the hypothesis. If all the predictions made from a hypothesis turn out to be true, then the hypothesis is called a "scientific law."

## Two Kinds of Reasoning

The kind of reasoning that is used in the game of "draw your own conclusion" is called *deductive reasoning*. The kind of reasoning that is used in the game of "as if" is called *inductive reasoning*. Deductive reasoning and inductive reasoning are the chief methods we use for figuring out new knowledge from old knowledge.

## The Art of Thinking

The games you have played in this book were designed to help you see the difference between clear thinking and confused thinking, and between straight thinking (valid reasoning) and crooked thinking (invalid reasoning). They have given you an introduction to the subject called *logic*, which deals with the art of thinking clearly and straight. What you have learned about logic in this book is only a small beginning. You will continue to learn more about logic through your daily experience. Perhaps some day, too, you will take a course in logic, or read a more advanced book on the subject.

*Answers to Brain Teasers*

**Chapter I**
1. F, O.   2. T, R.   3. F, R.   4. T, O.   5. F, O.   6. T, O.
7. T, O.   8. T, R.   9. F, R.   10. T, O.
(The answers to questions 3, 8, and 9 can be checked in
THE WORLD ALMANAC.)

**Chapter II**

1. Page 15.   2. Nine.   3. Rule 2.   4. 28 minutes.   5. IC;
IID; IIIE; IVB or E.

## Chapter III

1. Suspend judgment until other scientists repeat this experiment. 2. Examine the minutes of the meeting, if they exist. Interview the people who were at the meeting. 3. No. Since so many new discoveries are made every year in particle physics, an article that is 15 years old is out of date. He should also consult recent articles in magazines like SCIENCE, SCIENTIFIC AMERICAN, or THE AMERICAN SCIENTIST.

## Chapter IV

1. pitcher  2. left  3. bark  4. comb  5. eye  6. bat  7. trunk  8. picket  9. nut  10. pick  11. present  12. brush  13. mail  14. pool  15. point  16. loaf  17. page  18. mine  19. case  20. rock  21. tire, b.  22. blow, a.  23. ball, b.  24. jam, b.  25. lap, a.  26. nap, b.  27. lock, b.  28. grain, a.  29. hide, b.  30. bit, a.  31. fired  32. rare  33. chest  34. raising cane (Cain)  35. boxer  36. spotted  37. struck  38. with great pains
39. A boy who is often late is required to bring a parent to school. A boy who comes late is often required to bring a parent to school.  40. The skies are clear all day. The skies are clear for at least part of the day.  41. She removed the rug from the room and swept the room. She removed the rug from the room and swept the rug.
42. He called the dog, put the newspaper into the dog's mouth, and started back home.  43. Every morning he takes a run and then a shower bath.  44. The police department closed its books today in the case of Jane Grant, who disappeared seven years ago. Miss Grant was the daughter of Dr. Samuel Grant.  45. When I was six years old, my grandfather died.  46. The set of all residents of the United States. (All Vermonters belong to this larger

set.)   47. The set of all colors.   48. The set of all things we call "furniture."   49. The set of all writing implements. 50. The set of all children.   51. B, D, O, P, Q, R   52. D, O, P, Q, R   53. A, E, F, H, I, K, L, M, N, T, V, W, X, Y, Z 54. L, T, V, X   55. A, F, H, K, N, Y, Z   56. Yes.   57. No. 58. The universe of discourse is the set of all animals. A is the set of animals that are birds. B is the set of animals that have wings.   59. The universe of discourse is the set of all animals. A is the set of animals that are insects. B is the set of animals that have six legs.   60. The universe of discourse is the set of all animals. A is the set of animals that are frogs. B is the set of animals that can swim.

61. a) the set of all quadrilaterals  b) the set of all polygons  c) having four sides   62. a) the set of all chairs  b) the set of all seats  c) having a back and four legs   63. a) the set of all ultraviolet rays  b) the set of all electromagnetic rays  c) having a wavelength shorter than that of visible light and longer than that of x-rays   64. A rectangle is a quadrilateral whose angles are right angles.   65. The number 3 is one more than 2.

66. The universe of discourse is the set of pupils in my class. Assertion 1: There is a boy named Fred in my class. Assertion 2: Fred is a member of the set of people in my class who sit next to me.   67. The universe of discourse is a certain baseball team. Assertion 1: There is a boy named John on the team. Assertion 2: John is a member of the set of people on the team who play first base.

68. runs faster than   69. is the mother of   70. is less than 71. The hose is not connected to the water faucet.

72. The rear wheel has no spokes.

73. The middle rungs of the ladder are missing.

74. There are no ropes supporting the right end of the scaffold.

75. The horns of the crescent moon should point away from the sun.

76. Since all stars are further from the earth than the moon is, no star can be in front of the moon. The moon blocks from view any star that is behind it. So it is impossible to see a star between the horns of a crescent moon.

77. When you see a rainbow across the sky, the sun is behind you.

78. 0, 1, 2, 3   79. 0, 3, 6, 9   80. 25, 24, 30, 29

81. 8, 9, 10, 11   82. 13, 15, 17, 19   83. 36, 49, 64, 81

84. 7, 6, 8, 7   85. 72, 90, 110, 132   86. 36, 45, 55, 66

87. 6, 36, 7, 49   88. 34, 55, 89, 144   89. 64, 128, 256, 512

90. 22, 24, 25, 28   91. 13, 15, 8, 17   92. 5, 3125, 6, 46656

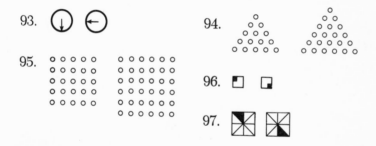

93.

94.

95.

96.

97.

98. short   99. way   100. calf   101. honey or wax

102. swim   103. proposition   104. false proposition

105. nonsense   106. nonsense   107. true proposition

108. nonsense   109. true proposition   110. false proposition   111. nonsense   112. nonsense   113. true proposition

114. false proposition   115. nonsense

## Chapter V

1.   U = residents of the United States
C = American citizens

2.  U = residents of Chicago
M = males

3.  U = living things
A = animals

4.  U = animals
T = three-legged robins

5.  U = animals
M = monkeys

6.  U = animals
P = phoenixes

7. Comp A = nonanimals (plants)  8. Comp C = noncitizens (aliens)  9. Comp A = nonadults (children)

10.  11.

12.

13. Some rectangles are not squares.
14. There are no books that are not bound.
15. There are no girls at Adams High School.
16. Some girls are pretty.

17. 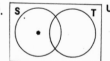 18.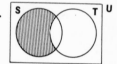

19. 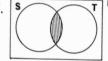 20.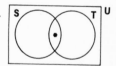

**Chapter VI**
1. compound   2. simple   3. simple   4. compound
5. compound

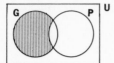

U = living things
G = grasses
P = plants

7.

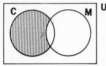

U = animals
C = cats
M = mammals

8.

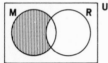

U = animals
M = mice
R = rodents

9. All chairs are seats.   10. All pencils are writing implements.

11. All cows are four legged animals.

12.

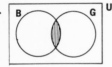

U = people
B = boys
G = girls

13.

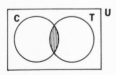

U = plane figures
C = circles
T = triangles

14.

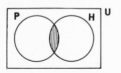

U = home furnishings
P = pillows
H = hard things

15. No horses are horned animals.   16. No boys are liars.
17. No girls are truants.

18.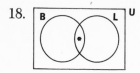

U = people
B = boys
L = liars

19.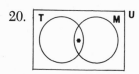

U = people
B = businessmen
T = thieves

20.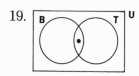

U = people
T = thieves
M = murderers

21. Some wives are good cooks; or, some good cooks are wives.   22. Some men are photographers; or, some photographers are men.   23. Some women are mothers; or, some mothers are women.

24.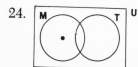

U = people
M = men
T = thieves

25.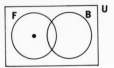

U = animals
F = flying animals
B = birds

26.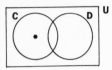

U = animals
C = cats
D = dogs

27. Some acquaintances are not friends.  28. Some ducks are not wild (animals).  29. Some Americans are not farmers.

30.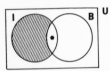

U = children
I = the baby
B = boys

31.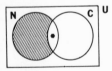

U = political units
N = New York
C = cities

32.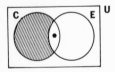

U = trees
C = the tree at the corner
E = elms

33. That man is an Indian.  34. Frank is an athlete.
35. Caesar is a Roman.

142

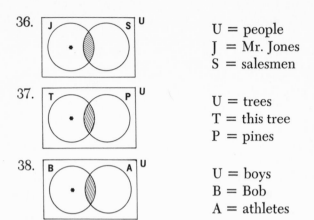

36.

U = people
J = Mr. Jones
S = salesmen

37.

U = trees
T = this tree
P = pines

38.

U = boys
B = Bob
A = athletes

39. Typing is not a required subject.  40. Peter is not a good dancer.

41. Dacron is not a natural fiber.

42. Some boys are eagle scouts. (Some A are B.)

43. Some high school graduates are not people who go to college. (Some A are not B.)

44. All girls are people who like to play with dolls. (All A are B.)

45. Some people elected to Congress are men. (Some A are not B.)

46. No Democrats are Republicans; or, no Republicans are Democrats. (No A are B.)

47. All people whose parents have blue eyes are people who have blue eyes. (All A are B.)

48. All people who wish to are people who may try out for the team. (All A are B.)

49. All carpenters are people who use hammers. (All A are B.)

50. Some Americans are people who live in cities. (Some A are B.)

51. No nonchickens are things that are here. (No A are B.)

52. Some girls in the class are girl scouts.

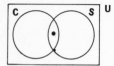

U = girls
C = girls in the class
S = girl scouts

53. All things worth doing are things worth doing well.

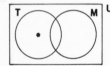

U = actions
V = things worth doing
W = things worth doing well

54. Some people who wear trousers are not men.

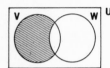

U = people
T = people who wear trousers
M = men

55. John is a school hater.

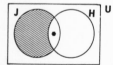

U = people
J = John
H = school haters

56. Some cowboy movies are dull movies.   57. All shoes are things made of leather.   58. Some British coins are not

round coins.   59. Einstein is a physicist.   60. No women are Supreme Court judges.   61. Some   62. All   63. All 64. No   65. Some   66. No   67. All   68. Some   69. All 70. Some

## Chapter VII
1.

| True | z L x, x L y, z L y |
|------|---------------------|
| False | x L x, y L y, z L z, x L z, y L x, y L z |

2. John H John, *John H Mary*, John H Tom, John H Bob, Mary H John, Mary H Mary, Mary H Tom, Mary H Bob, Tom H John, Tom H Mary, Tom H Tom, Tom H Bob, Bob H John, Bob H Mary, Bob H Tom, Bob H. Bob
3. John M Mary, Mary M John.
4. Tom B Bob, Bob B Tom.
5. John O Mary, John O Tom, John O Bob, Mary O Tom, Mary O Bob, Tom O Bob.
6. John C John, Tom C Tom, John C Tom, Tom C John, Mary C Mary, Bob C Bob, Mary C Bob, Bob C Mary.
7. No.   8. No.   9. No.   10. Yes.   11. Yes.   12. No. 13 Yes.   14. Yes.   15. No.   16. No.   17. Yes; yes.

## Chapter VIII
1. Invalid

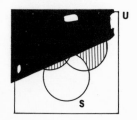

U = animals
A = ants
I = insects
S = six-legged animals

## 2. Valid

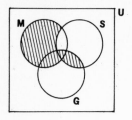

U = people
M = miners
S = stingy people
G = generous people

## 3. Valid

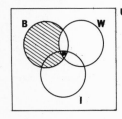

U = people
H = Mrs. Hag
W = witches
B = broom riders

## 4. Valid

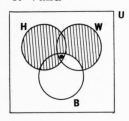

U = animals
B = butterflies
W = winged animals
I = insects

## 5. Invalid

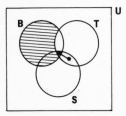

U = animals
B = birds
T = two-legged animals
S = swimmers

146

## 6. Valid

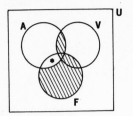

U = residents of the U. S. A.
A = aliens
V = voters
F = Mr. French

## 7. Valid

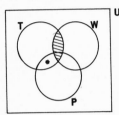

U = living things
T = trees
W = walking things
P = plants

## 8. Invalid

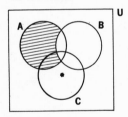

## 9. Invalid

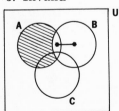

147

## 10. Valid

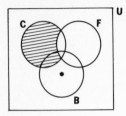

U = animals
C = crows
F = flying animals
B = birds

## 11.

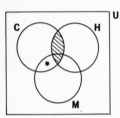

U = animals
C = cats
H = horned animals
M = mammals

Conclusion: Some mammals do not have horns.

## 12.

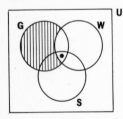

U = things, real or imaginary
G = goops
W = wowsies
S = serps

Conclusion: Some serps are wowsies.
Also, some wowsies are serps.

148

13.

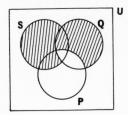

U = plane figures
S = squares
Q = quadrilaterals
P = polygons

Conclusion: **All squares are polygons.**

14.

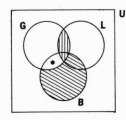

U = people
G = gentlemen
L = liars
B = Mr. Brown

Conclusion: Mr. Brown is not a liar.

15.

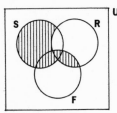

U = animals
S = squirrels
R = rodents
F = fish

Conclusion: No squirrel is a fish.
　　　　　Also, no fish is a squirrel.

16.

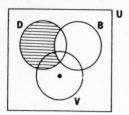

U = animals
D = ducks
B = birds
V = vertebrates

Conclusion: Some vertebrates are not ducks.

17.

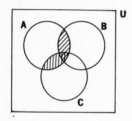

No conclusion.

18.

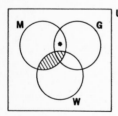

U = people
M = men
G = ugly people
W = women

Conclusion: Some ugly people are not women.

19.

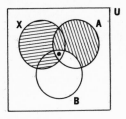

Conclusion: X is a B.

20.

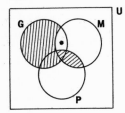

U = people
G = Dr. Gauss
M = mathematicians
P = pygmies

Conclusion: Dr. Gauss is not a pygmy.

21. True   22. False. President Kennedy was a Catholic.
23. False. Hawaii is not in North America.   24. True.
25. False. The Civil War and part of the War of 1812 were
    fought on United States soil.

## Chapter IX

(Note: One solution is given for each of the puzzles 1 through 20. Other solutions are also possible.)

1.

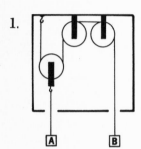

2.

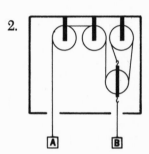

3.

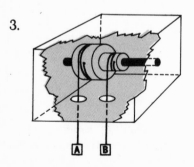

In answers 4 to 7 the arrow shows the direction in which the eye sees. M indicates a mirror.

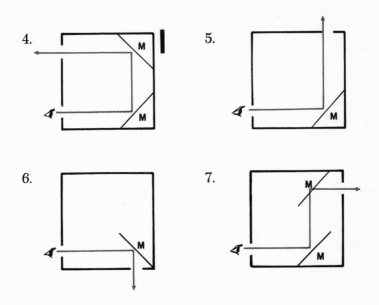

8. Two cats going over a fence.   9. A woman on her knees washing the floor.   10. A steamship below the horizon.   11. The old oaken bucket seen from the bottom of the well.   12. A motorcycle coming toward you on a dark road at night.   13. A wildcat in a cave.   14. Birds sitting on telephone wires.   15. A worm on a fish-hook in water. 16. A little boy blowing up a big balloon.   17. It looks as if the man was caught in the rain.   18. It looks as if the cat knocked the vase off the book case.   19. It looks as if the man was tripped by the dog chasing the cat.   20. It looks as if the cat knocked the milk bottle over and drank some of the spilled milk.

*Index*

# *Index*

*About the Author*

IRVING ADLER for many years was the kind of teacher who made everything so clear, so fascinating that students found themselves looking forward to classes and becoming enthusiastic about all kinds of outside projects. Formerly an instructor in mathematics at Columbia University and Bennington College and chairman of the mathematics department of a New York City high school, he now devotes his time to writing books and speaking at meetings and conferences on mathematics throughout the country. He is a member of the Advisory Committee on Mathematics for the Non-College-Bound (a committee of the National Council of Teachers of Mathematics).